AMERICA'S

by
DONALD W. COX, Ed.D.

Illustrated by
Dwight Dobbins

Explorers

of

Space

Including a Special Report on UFO's

INCORPORATED

MAPLEWOOD, NEW JERSEY

This book was published by Hammond Incorporated under the following editorial direction: Ernest J. Dupuy, *Associate Editor;* Emily D. Highfield, *Copy Editor;* Isabelle Reid, *Book Designer* and Gunars J. Rutins, *Map Editor.* Original art by Dwight Dobbins. Assisting in the preparation of copy were Dorothy Bacheller and Jean Talbot.

All creative operations were coordinated by Andrew F. Kuber in cooperation with Herbert Pierce, *Director of Cartographic Arts* and E. V. Ballman, *Director of Photography.* Production was under the supervision of Harvey Brittle.

Contents

Introduction	8
Robert H. Goddard	10
James H. Wyld	14
Theodore von Kármán	18
Charles E. Yeager	22
John P. Stapp	26
Wernher von Braun	30
John R. Pierce	34
Alan B. Shepard Jr.	38
Virgil I. Grissom	42
John H. Glenn Jr.	46
Christopher C. Kraft Jr.	50
William H. Pickering	54
Edward H. White II	58
Robert J. Parks	62
John W. Young — Michael Collins	66
Frank D. Drake	70
Special Report on UFO's	74
Chronology of U.S. Manned Space Flights	88
Further Reading	89
Glossary	90
Index	92
Credits	93

Introduction

It hardly seems possible that actually a full decade has passed since the Space Age was born on October 4, 1957. Prior to the launching of the first Sputniks, Explorers and Vanguards, America had no authentic national space heroes. We did boast a small number of so-called "backyard rocketry" engineers and prophets whose names were known mainly to a tiny minority of our citizenry who were interested in the subject during the pre-Space Age era.

Some of these names, like Dr. Robert Goddard and Dr. Wernher von Braun, who later blossomed into wider national prominence because of their pioneering work and their prophecies made before 1957, are described in the early chapters of this book. But it was the advent of manned space flight, beginning in 1961, that ushered in a new type of national and international space hero — the astronaut and his earthbound comrade, the aerospace engineer. A selection of some of the more notable names in this new galaxy are included.

The heroes of the Mercury and Gemini programs naturally are given the bulk of attention since their feats are already an important part of space history. Thus, you will find portraits of Alan Shepard, our first man in space, and John Glenn, our first astronaut to orbit the earth, and also some of the later Gemini astronauts such as Edward White. Not all of the brave astronauts who have contributed to our space effort could be delineated but highlights of their exploits are given in a Chronology of U.S. Manned Space Flights in the appendix.

Our infant man-in-space program, beginning with the one-man Mercury program in 1961, then progressing to the more sophisticated two-man Gemini astronaut program in 1965 and 1966, has all been aimed at achieving a step-by-step progression toward the fulfillment of the three-man Apollo lunar effort which will begin in early 1968 and culminate hopefully in placing two Americans on the moon by 1969.

It is too early to predict who those first lucky astronauts will be — to have the privilege of first setting foot on the lunar surface which, in the late President Kennedy's words would make them "our representatives on the moon." However, it is not too early to bestow credit on those unsung heroes on the ground who will help make this dramatic event possible. For this reason, the reader will find among our profiles such persons as Christopher Kraft, the NASA Flight Director, and Robert Parks, the Chief of the Surveyor program.

Space does not permit the portrayal of some of the other hard working space administrators, medical doctors and technicians who have not received equal public acclaim with the more glamorous astronauts, but who should rightfully share in the success of our past and future manned space missions. It is appropriate that some of the more prominent and deserving of these non-flying space heroes be mentioned here in order to put those profiled-in-depth in their proper perspective.

Any roster of the behind-the-scenes heroes who are glued to the ground by their profession would include among others:

• *James Webb,* the Administrator of NASA since 1961, who heads a gigantic complex enterprise of over 400,000 people, located around the world, working in both public and private space facilities, to help insure the safety and success of our manned and unmanned civilian space efforts.

• *Dr. Hugh Dryden,* the late Deputy Administrator of the National Aeronautics and Space Administration, from 1958 until his death on December 2, 1965, one of the pioneers in the development of our first guided missile and supersonic aircraft who worked vigorously toward the advancement of our manned space programs.

• *Dr. Robert Gilruth,* the quiet, balding Director of the Manned Spacecraft Center at Houston, which oversees the operation of Project Apollo as it did the earlier Mercury and Gemini programs.

• *Walter Williams,* now with the Aerospace Corporation, who was in charge of the Mercury project under Gilruth and helped to father six successful flights before the completion of that first step in our manned space program.

• *Dr. D. Brainerd Holmes,* NASA's first Administrator for Manned Space Flight activities who helped get the Apollo Saturn man-to-the-moon program rolling before returning to private industry.

• *Dr. George Mueller,* the scholarly successor to Holmes, who is the present overseer of all manned space activities at NASA headquarters in Washington.

• *Dr. William Douglas* and *Lt. Col. Stanley White, M.D.,* the two original space medical doctors who constantly kept watch over the physical condition of their star pupils — the Mercury astronauts.

Obviously this list is far from complete, but it should present a preview of a possible sequel to this book on "The Men Behind the Spacemen." Meanwhile, those Americans profiled in the following pages have been chosen as worthy candidates for any officially designated U.S. Space Hall of Fame, should such an institution ever be established.

These men are the forerunners of the space engineers and astronauts who will, in the future, be making longer space voyages to the moon, the planets and eventually the stars. By a quirk of fate, the initial selection has been restricted to members of the male sex since no women have as yet played a prominent role in our expanding astronautical programs. In time, however, the names of women will undoubtedly be added to our list of space heroes. (The Russians have already orbited at least one woman — Soviet Cosmonaut Valentina Tereshkova, who later married Major Andrian Nikolaev. He

had previously orbited the earth in a Vostok capsule. Both are space heroes in the Soviet Union.)

It is in the realm of possibility that one day astronauts sent out into space from their earthbound home will contact civilized creatures from another world. Whether they be American or Russian astronauts who make the contact will not be as important as the link-up itself. For communication with other rational creatures in deep space, which reputable astronomers tell us exist in other star systems beyond our own, is a virtual certainty within the next 100 years.

For this reason, in anticipation of such an historic event of interstellar communication, which will be even more dramatic than a man from earth landing on the dead moon, a Special Report on Unidentified Flying Objects has been made a part of this book. This section provides a brief objective overview of the UFO (flying saucer) controversy. The possibility of a UFO crossing the path of astronauts in the future may give us some worthwhile clues as to their mysterious origins. The last two profile chapters, covering possible UFO sightings by Gemini astronauts Young and Collins in mid-1966 and the attempts made to contact other worlds under Project Ozma by the astronomer, Dr. Frank Drake, provide a natural bridge to this section.

All of the American space heroes who appear in the following pages have one trait in common: *courage* — that rare characteristic exhibited by the political leaders who graced the pages of the late President John Kennedy's Pulitzer Prize work, "Profiles in Courage." Since he showed this quality of courage himself in launching us on a major effort in 1961 to put an American man on the moon in this decade, it is proper that we add his name to the list of national space heroes:

• *John Fitzgerald Kennedy,* for establishing the first major goal of America's manned space program, Project Apollo, our attempt to land a man on the moon in this decade.

Robert H. Goddard
Father of Modern Rocketry

Although the world recognizes the late Russian mathematics teacher, Konstantin Edwardvich Tsiolkovsky, as the "Father of Spaceflight," an American physics professor is accorded a similar honor as the "Father of Modern Rocketry." His name is Robert Hutchings Goddard and his pioneering experiments conducted in the first half of the twentieth century paved the way for the blossoming of the Space Age in the latter half of the same century.

His career, like that of most prophets and visionaries, who lived in advance of the innovations which they promoted, was studded with many setbacks and successes. He was often derided by his critics who used such slurring titles to describe him as "Mooney" Goddard — because of his pre-occupation with the project of sending an unmanned rocket to our lunar satellite. But these diatribes did not deter him from the pursuit of his tasks.

In 1913, after graduating from college, he became seriously ill with tuberculosis. At one point, the doctors gave him only two weeks to live. But the indomitable Goddard fooled them. "I felt I had to stay alive to complete my work on rocketry," he said with a wan smile. Although still so weakened by the disease that he could hardly hold his pen, Goddard spent the rest of 1913 writing down his basic ideas and theories of rocketry in a notebook before he had even tested a single live rocket on a launching platform. He was so sure of his theories that he took out two U.S. Government patents to cover them. By 1919, while earning his living as an unassuming physics professor at Clark University in Worcester, Massachusetts, Goddard published his first and most famous paper, "A Method of Reaching Extreme Altitudes." This short paper, prepared with the aid of a small grant from the Smithsonian Institution in Washington, was to revolutionize the whole approach to rocketry and plant the seed for the birth of the Space Age almost 40 years later.

Goddard's human characteristic of working alone and in silence made it possible for the German, Hermann Oberth, to receive most of the initial credit and worldwide reputation as the innovator of the idea that liquid-fueled rockets were superior to the old-fashioned, powder type missiles. Goddard was not overly concerned that the European was being acclaimed as the pioneer exponent of this new type of rocket since his own first experiments with alcohol and gasoline fuels were unsatisfactory. After his marriage to the Secretary to the President of Clark University, Esther Kisk (Goddard), in June 1924, Goddard found a mate, who for the next 20 years served as his official photographer, devotee, and note-taker of his experiments.

After several failures, Goddard abandoned his earlier approaches to perfecting a liquid-fueled rocket and started to experiment with liquid oxygen's expansion peculiarities, as it turns back to a gas at temperatures below 297 degrees F., to pressurize his fuel tanks. He used the pressure of the liquid oxygen (LOX) to force both his oxidizer and the gasoline into the rocket's firing chamber. By the early spring of 1926, Goddard felt that his new rocket was ready for an actual test. On March 16th, with the help of his wife and two assistants from the University, Goddard took his strange-looking, 10-foot-long contraption out to the farm of his Aunt Effie Ward in nearby Auburn. The day was clear and cold with a light covering of snow on the ground, ideal weather for the experiment.

When the fuel tanks had been charged, Goddard gave the signal and a simple blow-torch ignited the fuel (instead of the complicated electrical igniters used in today's more complex rockets). The LOX and gasoline erupted with a roar, sending the ungainly looking rocket upward for two and a half seconds, until its fuel was exhausted. Before it fell back to earth a few moments later, it had ascended to a height of 41 feet and reached a speed of 60 miles per hour. Thus the age of modern rocketry had begun. (Today a stone tablet marks the historic spot of the world's first liquid rocket ascent on what is now a golf course.)

Two months later, Goddard reported his rocket success to the Smithsonian Institution, but no public notice was made of the shot until three years had passed. Meanwhile, on his next rocket flight conducted in July on his Aunt Effie's farm, some unfortunate repercussions arose as a result of the noise generated by his experiment. The following day, July 17th, *The New York Times* described the commotion with this story:

METEOR-LIKE ROCKET STARTLES WORCESTER

Clark Professor's Test of a New
Propellent to Explore Air Strata
Brings Police to Scene

WORCESTER, July 17—A rocket designed by Professor Robert H. Goddard of Clark University, in his experiments to explore upper air strata, was sent through the air in an isolated part of Worcester this afternoon like a flaming meteor, with a roar heard for two miles around.

The noise was such that scores of residents called Police Headquarters, saying that an airplane was shooting along afire. Two police ambulances scoured the section looking for victims and an airplane left Grafton airport to aid in the search . . .

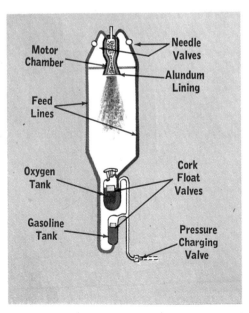

Above diagram shows simplicity of early Goddard rocket. Motor was fueled with gasoline and liquid oxygen fed through a simple pump system and ignited with a blow torch.

Although Goddard stated to the press that this was just another in a series of meteorological and atmospheric experiments, with no attempt being made to reach the moon, the local townspeople were not convinced. They brought pressure on him which eventually forced the physics professor to seek another, more remote, test site for his experiments. Although he was still being supported with a modest grant from the Smithsonian Institution, Goddard needed more money to continue his experiments. Fortunately, Charles A. Lindbergh, who had recently made his famous solo airplane flight across the Atlantic in 1927, had read about the "Moon Man's" noisy rocket and his interest was aroused.

Dr. Goddard stands next to his rocket on day of historic flight at Aunt Effie's farm.

After making a visit to the campus at Clark to see for himself what was actually happening, Col. Lindbergh came away convinced that Goddard was on to something worthwhile. He thereupon convinced his philanthropic friend, Daniel Guggenheim, long a supporter of aeronautical research, to back Goddard with a $25,000 grant to continue his experiments. This welcome support enabled Goddard to take a two-year leave of absence from his teaching to devote full time to his rocketry experiments.

Finding a more suitable place to conduct his rocket launchings in the desert wastes near Roswell, New Mexico, Goddard set up a small workshop there in 1930, the same year that the Smithsonian published the reports of his experiments made four years before at Auburn.

During the decade of the thirties, Goddard, his wife Esther, and a few assistants conducted a series of experiments with large liquid-fueled rockets on the Mescalero Ranch, sending them up to heights of several thousand feet and speeds of over 500 miles per hour. It was in New Mexico that Goddard licked the stabilization problem through the use of gyroscopes — a problem that had plagued Congreve in the eighteenth century, and all the rocket enthusiasts who had experimented earlier.

After a short respite back in Massachusetts, due to a lack of funds to continue his experiments during the depression, Goddard and his crew returned to the ranch in 1934, where he re-opened his workshop and built larger rockets. On March 28, 1935, his new single-stage liquid-fueled projectile soared 13,000 feet over New Mexico at a speed of 550 miles per hour before crashing back to earth. In the late thirties, Goddard also perfected a rocket steering system and an advanced turbo-pump system to feed the fuel to his rockets.

But the baldheaded, ex-professor's latest success was compromised by his inability to attain any substantial government development contract from either the Army or the Navy. Goddard's mistake was his preference for working alone. He did not foresee the necessity of an integrated team effort to design and construct the large rocket and satellite boosters of today. As the last of the old breed of individualistic inventors of the Edison Era, Goddard helped to create a complex new field of technology that could be properly handled only by groups of people and industries working in tandem, and not by solo inventors working by themselves in attics, cellars, and garages.

Despite his successes, he was still a disillusioned man. On August 10, 1945, four days before the surrender of Japan, he died following a throat operation for cancer at Johns Hopkins Hospital in Baltimore. Although he had continued to work until the end of his life on what he called the "most fascinating problem in applied physics," he was disheartened by the "lack of enthusiasm in dignified and sophisticated engineering circles about the subject of projection beyond the earth."

His fellow countrymen waited almost 15 years to finally pay the proper tribute to the memory of the space age pioneer by dedicating a giant multi-million dollar NASA space-flight center in his honor at Greenbelt, Md., and awarding his widow over $1,000,000 for the patent rights to 214 of his basic inventions.

At the dedication of the Robert H. Goddard Rocket and Space Wing of the Roswell, New Mexico, Museum and Art Center in 1959, Dr. Wernher von Braun, the noted German-American space scientist, praised the American rocket pioneer as one of those rare "visionary dreamers" who have accomplished so much for the edification and benefit of mankind. He referred to Dr. Goddard as his boyhood hero at the opening of a collection of rocket motors and other memorabilia used by the bald, mustachioed rocket genius in his experiments conducted at nearby White Sands a quarter century earlier. Von Braun pointed out that America would undoubtedly have enjoyed unchallenged leadership in space exploration during the first years of the Space Age if adequate support and recognition had been accorded Robert Goddard, the man who did so much to make today's accomplishments in the fields of both rocketry and astronautics possible.

Von Braun related how Goddard had submitted an article for publication back in 1907 suggesting that atomic energy would one day propel a rocket ship into interplanetary space. The magazine editor declined the paper with thanks and told him: "the speculation is interesting, but the impossibility of ever doing it is so certain that it is not practically useful. You have written well and clearly but not helpfully to science as I see it."

Unfortunately, that forgotten editor did not foresee the "practical" applications of Goddard's ideas and contributions, which von Braun summarized so well as providing "a solid basis for the progressive development of rocketry as the means to achieve his shining ambition — the exploration of the space and regions where the silent planets, stars and galaxies await the adventurers who follow in his giant footsteps."

Goddard (left) and assistants check one of his last rockets at Roswell, New Mexico, in 1940.

James H. Wyld

Inventor of the First Liquid Rocket Engine for Airplane Propulsion

Although Goddard had successfully built and fired the first unmanned liquid-fueled rocket engines in the twenties and thirties, four other Americans advanced us a step farther in the new technology with the development of the first man-carrying rocket engine in the forties. One of these men, James Wyld, added a unique contribution of his own to the infant rocketry state-of-the-art which enabled Air Force Captain Charles Yeager, at the controls of the famed Bell X–1, to become the first person of any nationality to fly faster than the speed of sound.

In the late thirties, two young mechanical engineers, John Shesta and James H. Wyld of New York City, constructed a small rocket test stand using cheap machine tools bought from a Sears Roebuck mail order catalogue. After losing their jobs in the 1938 business recession, they were able to devote full time to their hobby of rocket propulsion. Wyld lived largely on chop suey and spaghetti as the basis of his economy diet in order to carry on their experiments, while his partner subsisted on rye bread and lard.

All their savings were dissipated within a year and they regretfully had to give up their experiments temporarily in order to seek work, but not before they had successfully run a number of tests of a small liquid-fueled rocket engine that had been designed and constructed by Wyld. When Wyld left for a job in the midwest, the two men were not able to meet again for three years.

Meanwhile, the infant American Rocket Society was looking for an adequate site for engine testing and one of their more enthusiastic members, Lovell Lawrence, Jr., scoured the backwoods of northern New Jersey until he found a suitable site near the Wanaque Reservoir, where rockets might be fired without interference by either state or local police. After lashing Wyld's small rocket engine to the test stand and running it several times, Lawrence got the idea that the U.S. Government might be interested in this gadget. World War II had already started in Europe and he foresaw possible military uses for the invention. By this time, Wyld had returned to the East.

One evening a rump meeting was held in the home of Shesta's brother-in-law. Present were a subway conductor, Franklin Pierce, two engineers, Wyld and Shesta, and a serviceman for International Business Machines, Lawrence. By midnight, when the meeting broke up, a new company was born. Electing Lawrence the President, the four incorporators named their new company Reaction Motors, Inc. Their plant consisted of half of an upper floor of John Shesta's brother-in-law's garage in North Arlington, N. J., "which was about as large as a spacious outhouse," said Wyld.

Lawrence immediately went to Washington to try to persuade the Navy to send a representative up to New Jersey to see a demonstration of Wyld's regenerative cooled engine which was the new com-

First lightweight commercial rocket engine designed by Wyld developed 100 pounds of thrust. At right is rocket test stand of Wyld and Shesta.

pany's only asset. Wyld's unique contribution to the advance of the infant rocket technology was to run small pipes through the engine's thrust chamber and then pump unburned fuel (alcohol or gasoline) through these pipes before igniting it with the liquid oxygen or fuming nitric acid mixture at the shower head nozzle. The fuel flowing through the pipes would cool the chamber and keep it from overheating or melting in the high, thousand-degree temperature periods during a firing. (This principle is still used today in large liquid-fueled rockets.)

The idea of a regenerative cooled rocket engine was not new. Hermann Oberth, the German rocket expert, had first proposed such a system in 1923. The regenerative cooled engine made its first appearance, in practice, in a small motor constructed in 1933 by Harry W. Bull of Syracuse, N.Y., a fellow member with Wyld in the American Rocket Society. Bull circulated gasoline only through the nozzle part of the motor to keep it cool. But the motor proved hazardous for other reasons and Bull dropped his experiments. Wyld's other A.R.S. friend, John Shesta, had tried a water-cooled jacket around a four nozzle rocket in 1934 but this approach proved impractical due to the increased weight.

Wyld produced the first practical motor

design applying regenerative cooling to all parts of the motor. His design solved the dilemma of achieving safety and simplicity without sacrificing weight. The Wyld regenerative cooled rocket engine was so efficient that after its first static test firing in December 1938 the motor was cool enough to touch with a bare hand!

When Lt. Fink Fisher of the U.S. Navy witnessed the successful firing of the little engine during his visit to the North Jersey test site in late 1941, he promised to promote their fine, "Swiss watch-like" product with his superiors in Washington. Meanwhile, Wyld and Shesta also perfected a nitrogen gas pressurization system which eliminated the dangerous secondary explosions caused by pools of fuel forming on the bottom length of the horizontal firing chamber of their rockets. While the four rocket engine company stockholders were waiting for the Navy to come through with a small development contract, Pearl Harbor was attacked by the Japanese.

The day that would "live in infamy" brought about a real new sense of urgency to the work of the Reaction Motors concern. By pooling their savings and browbeating relatives, the four determined men raised $5,000 among themselves — enough to rent larger quarters in an empty store-

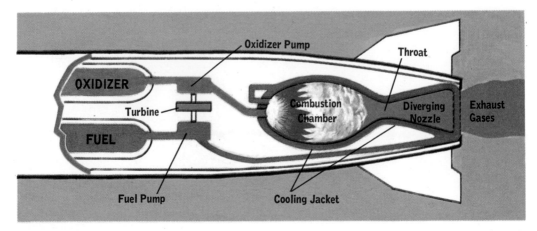

Regenerative rocket engine is cooled by pumping fuel around combustion chamber and nozzle. The raised temperature of the fuel also facilitates ignition.

room in Pompton Lakes, N. J., and buy some necessary machine shop equipment. They were even too busy to remove the old sign from their front window. This read: "Pat's Tailor Shop," and made it difficult for passersby to reconcile the peculiar whirring sounds and violent hammering which emanated from behind the storefront with the real function of the sign.

Before they moved out of the tailor shop a year later, the four men had built ten experimental liquid rocket engines, ranging from 50 to 1,000 pounds of thrust. By May 1943 successful runs were being made at up to 3400 pounds of thrust. This work was being accomplished by a team of less than twenty men working with limited funds. Later, Wyld was to observe that "the corresponding German development work in 1934–1938, which was only disclosed after the end of the war, had required 4 years' work by several dozen men and must have cost at least a million dollars, resulting in a motor having the same thrust as the American design, but a much poorer jet velocity. This seems a convincing proof that the lack of progress of American rocket research had not been due to any inherent lack of technical skill, but was caused solely by the prevailing attitude of ridicule and indifference to the whole subject which blocked almost all advance for at least ten years."

When the Navy renewed their contract, they were able to move into larger quarters — an old cow barn in nearby Pompton Plains where they started to work on a 6,000-pound thrust engine. The local townspeople were not aware that a new era in rocketry and aviation had begun in their own backyard.

As the 6,000-pound thrust engine was being tested for the first time in a sand pit located just outside of town, sidewalks cracked and plaster broke off the walls, and dishes fell in several local homes. Housewives and angry citizens screamed for revenge at the four harebrained noisemakers and the town council soon voted to bring a suit for $50,000 in damages against Reaction Motors. Since this was ten times the amount of the capitalization of their company, Lawrence, Pierce, Wyld, and Shesta had but one alternative — get out of town.

So, they packed up their tools and moved from town-to-town in North Jersey, from abandoned barns to empty garages, in search of a safe sanctuary where they would not be harassed and hounded by the local citizenry. Even the woods around the Wanaque Reservoir no longer provided a secluded haven for their work, for the roar of their rocket engines could be heard for miles. With these irate-citizenry stumbling blocks constantly in front of them, it was a miracle that the young company survived to provide a successful 30,000-pound, liquid-thrust JATO (Jet Assisted Take-Off) unit for Navy planes and liquid-fueled engines for the Gorgon and Lark missiles.

Fortunately, the Naval Bureau of Aeronautics solved their problems when it decided to set up a government-owned rocket development laboratory at Lake Denmark, N. J. — a lonely spot in the hills that formerly had been a munitions dump. Reaction Motors was invited to lease space in this government property, where no one could complain of the embryonic firm's testing. At last they were protected from angry neighbors by tall steel fences.

The company now went to work with a vengeance, aided by a new Air Force contract, signed by Lawrence, to develop a rocket engine to power the revolutionary Bell X–1, the first supersonic airplane planned to fly faster than the speed of sound. Since no power plant had been chosen for the secret project, Lawrence optimistically promised the Air Force a demonstration on the as yet unbuilt and untried 6,000-pound rocket engine within a month. Parts of this prototype engine were lying around rusting on shelves, having been put there months earlier because of low priorities. Now they would prove useful!

Shesta, Wyld, and Pierce, with the help of a new assistant engineer, Ed Francisco, dug out the four rusted and decrepit-looking rocket tubes from the storeroom and went to work assembling the engine. Although they failed to sand away most of the rust on the outside of the tubes, they were elated to discover that the tubes themselves still operated. By adding new valves, ignition systems, and feed lines, they were able to work each tube into an acceptable firing shape.

When the four tubes finally were bound together with bailing wire and metal strips, the resulting engine gave the appearance of having just been picked up from a local junkyard. In order to cover up the rather depressing physical appearance of their engine, the four men splashed several coats of black paint over their work and dubbed it *Black Betsy*. Then they held their breath and notified the Air Force that they were ready to conduct a test demonstration of America's first man-carrying rocket engine.

Today *Black Betsy* is hung in the Smithsonian Institution in Washington, hidden inside of *Glamorous Glennis,* the original Bell X–1, which Major Charles Yeager flew to glory on October 14, 1947 — the first time that any man had flown supersonically. James Wyld, who was to die prematurely a few years later, lived long enough to see his offspring go down in history as a significant advance in man's reach for the stars.

The multi-cylinder, 6,000-pound thrust engine developed by Wyld's firm.

Theodore von Kármán
Impatient Visionary and Practical Scientist

In 1928, Harry Guggenheim, the eminent American philanthropist, used some of his father's foundation money to bring over to our shores a little known Hungarian aerodynamicist named Theodore von Kármán. The little, roly-poly bachelor genius was soon ensconced at the famed Guggenheim Aeronautical Laboratory, located at the California Institute of Technology, where he started to work in earnest on many of the experiments which were to revolutionize man's approach to supersonic flight both in the atmosphere and in space.

Von Kármán was born to Professor Maurice de Kármán in Budapest in 1881. His father won great acclaim for establishing the state school system in Hungary as well as a special plan for education of the members of the Royal House. When the Emperor Franz Joseph wished to bestow the high honor of "Excellence" on the Professor, Maurice declined, but he finally decided to accept the hereditary title of nobility for his family.

Young Theodore's remarkable gift of being able to perform difficult mathematical problems in his head brought a stern rebuke from his father who forbade him to "show off" before family gatherings. His father insisted on seeing that he received a well-rounded education from his tutors, thus saving him from becoming a mathematical freak. The elder Kármán exerted a strong influence on the boy, particularly in the realm of ideas, so that he could learn to have a clear and comprehensive picture of what happened in nature and why it happened, as well.

"One of my father's convictions," he related, "was that science is just the organization of our experiences—what we see, what we hear. So I have always been attracted by logical system. If there are contradictions, I cannot sleep until I understand why. I am not a gadgeteer, not an inventor in this sense; I am a systematic thinker. The greatest inspiration to me is to create order."

The young von Kármán soon found himself diverted into the growing field of aerodynamics upon the urging of a newspaperwoman who persuaded him to come out to an airport near Paris on a bleak morning in 1908 to witness the first airplane flight made by a Frenchman, Henri Farman. Although the Wright Brothers had already performed their historic flight at Kitty Hawk five years earlier, the event had not registered on the Europeans until Farman made his one kilometer circular flight around the suburban Paris airport. The recent graduate of the Royal Hungarian Technical University immediately became mesmerized by the problems of flight, particularly the impact of the wind on the wings and body of an airplane.

Von Kármán went on to do graduate work for his Ph.D. under the famed aerodynamicist, Ludwig Prandtl, at the University of Göttingen in Germany. He remained at the University for three more years as a teaching fellow, where he first became addicted to the parallels between the oscillations of water flowing around a cylinder and of wind around a curved wing. He reasoned that the workings of nature should not be fought, changed or overcome, but rather understood and turned to men's advantage. Out of his experiments came one of the major advancements in the science of aerodynamics — the von Kármán theory of Vortex Trails which explained the rotating motions and eddies behind a body, whether in water or air. This effect, von Kármán postulated, was the chief cause of drag or resistance, which turned out to be useful when trying to explain the stabilization of ships and aircraft as they moved about in their respective mediums.

He was next appointed to the prestigious post of Germany's newly established Aeronautical Institute of the University of Aachen. But the skies which he studied for their wind currents soon became blackened with the clouds of World War I and military orders thereupon determined his address for the next four years: The Austro–Hungarian Air Corps. His most productive portion of the war period was the time he spent developing a helicopter design with

two contra-rotating propellers. Although this contraption never flew, it marked another example of the vision of the man who foresaw by a whole generation the age of the whirlybirds.

Following the war, he returned to the University of Aachen, where his Aeronautical Institute became a mecca for the airminded. After almost a decade of distinguished work there, he moved to America where he took up his position at Cal Tech in Pasadena. That was to be his home for the rest of his life. America now possessed a top scientist equal to Europe's Prandtl.

Von Kármán never married, but lived with his favorite sister, Josephine, whom he fondly called Pipö. She served as his housekeeper and accompanied him to the United States when he accepted the offer of Harry Guggenheim to come to this country. Arriving in California, he accepted an associate post at the aerodynamical laboratory which was named after his benefactor. Within a year, this world's leading authority on wind tunnels was named Director of the GALCIT (Guggenheim Aeronautical Lab at Cal Tech).

In 1929, he played host to a distinguished visiting scientist from Boston, who

Dr. von Kármán confers with engineers and pilot before first JATO test flight at March Field, August 1941.

Capt. Homer Boushey's Ercoupe climbs steeply in JATO assisted takeoff.

inquired, "How does it happen you employ so many foreigners?" after being introduced to von Kármán's colleagues who came from such far-off places as China, Hungary, and India. The recent emigré, who was to become an American citizen himself in 1934, retorted indignantly: "What should I do? Hire a Navajo Indian?"

Von Kármán was one of the few modern geniuses who did not restrict himself to one speciality. He was interested in the totality of life, encompassing all fields of academic knowledge. His pattern of work followed a routine best summed up by his own anecdotal expression, "First comes articulation of the problem, then the complexities, then the disagreements, and finally the slivovitz plum brandy." This phrase marked a typical, fun-loving example of what his friends called "Kármániana." This logical thought process explained the evolution of his thinking from aeronautics to astronautics.

In 1936, von Kármán became the advisor, father-confessor, and cheerleader to a group of six Cal Tech researchers who dubbed themselves the Suicide Club. The name of the embryonic organization was a humorous reminder that its members were dealing in a new and dangerous endeavor —rockets. When Dr. Robert Millikan, the Nobel laureate and cosmic ray expert who headed Cal Tech, heard about this latest activity of his prize Hungarian professor, he threatened to remove him from his staff, according to student gossip. But von

Kármán was not to be deterred, and two years later his project achieved a status of respectability when General Henry H. Arnold, the head of the Army Air Corps, made a decision that his heavy bombers should have rockets to assist them on take-offs, thus increasing the margin of safety.

Both Cal Tech and MIT were given the opportunity to tackle the problem, but the noted Eastern technology citadel waived its rights to the West with the comment that von Kármán was the one to pursue "the Buck Rogers job with rockets." Soon, he had his first Air Corps contract for research and development of rockets. It totaled a munificent $1,000.

With his wit and skill, the professor approached the problem of shooting planes off the ground with no assurance of success. There were early misfires and premature explosions in his team's early experiments with jet-assisted-takeoff (JATO). Eventually, by 1940, all was ready to translate theory into practice. Captain Homer Boushey, of the USAF, (who later was to become a general), volunteered to be the human guinea pig to fly a light Ercoupe airplane, propelled by the burning fury of bottled explosives attached to its wingtips. When the six rockets ignited, the plane took off safely and Boushey made history as the first man to fly a rocket plane.

Despite his pre-war success, von Kármán discovered that in 1940 there was not one American corporation that could be persuaded to build rockets. Ever dauntless and ready to gamble on the future, he and five friends each put up $1,500 to create a new company to build rockets. They named it the Aerojet Engineering Co. (Today, this multibillion dollar enterprise, the Aerojet General Corp., is one of the giants of the aerospace industry.)

Notwithstanding the demand for rocket boosted takeoff JATO's, these devices were still looked upon by the military purely as adjuncts to existing planes. The rocket was still floundering in its infancy as a second priority, accessory item, when von Kármán approached the Pentagon in 1943 and urged the Army to institute a crash missile program in the best interest of the nation.

In 1944, during the latter days of World War II, von Kármán underwent a serious hernia operation brought on by the strain of his many activities. While recuperating at Lake George, N.Y., he received an urgent phone call from General Arnold asking him if he could meet him at La Guardia Airport during the following week to discuss a matter of vital importance.

He complied, and when he met the General, "Hap" Arnold whispered the succinct reason for the meeting. "World War III," he said. "I want to know what airpower can do to prevent it!" With World War II almost won, Arnold was concerned with the shape of aerial warfare in 10 to 20 years. "Jet propulsion, rockets, radar — what does it mean?" he queried.

"What do you want me to do?" von Kármán asked.

"Kármán, I want you to come to the Pentagon and form a group of scientists . . . and work out a blueprint for future research and development."

The Hungarian agreed with one proviso: "I will do it, General, so long as no one gives orders to me, and I don't have to give orders to anyone." The Air Corps chief agreed and the still convalescing scientist was soon off to Washington where he gathered together 31 top brains known as the Air Force Scientific Advisory Group. They traveled extensively around the United States, Europe and Japan, visiting various laboratories and universities and ultimately published a monumental twenty volume set of predictions called appropriately: *Toward New Horizons.*

Among the visionary projects detailed in that now famous 1944 von Kármán report were: an earth satellite, intercontinental rockets, anti-missile defense system, supersonic bombers and automatic celestial navigation equipment.

After receiving some 25 honorary degrees, this simple, fun-loving man undertook, at the age of 70, to conceive, organize and administer the most ambitious worldwide scientific group yet created by modern man — the NATO Advisory Group for Aeronautical Research and Development (AGARD). Von Kármán's work with the European group, which was facilitated by his fluency in seven languages, marked another high spot of his distinguished career. As chairman, he admirably filled the three-hat role of scientist, diplomat and raconteur extraordinary.

Von Kármán's strongly individualistic mind led to many new concepts of original scientific thinking that resulted in many important scientific breakthroughs later. His curiosity about all things and his courage to re-evaluate established theories led to this personal declaration made in mid-life: "I believe in the importance of space exploration. In 1922, one of the very well-known and very learned German professors gave a talk to the effect that it was impossible to leave the atmosphere and the gravitational field. I stood up and said, 'I am not a fantast. It is just a simple fact that one pound of kerosene has more energy than is necessary to take this one pound out of the gravitational field. It shows it is only a question of technology, progress and time.' "

Just before he died, in 1963, the 82-year-old von Kármán was honored at a White House ceremony where President Kennedy presented him with the Distinguished Service Medal, an honor bestowed on only a handful of our scientific giants. In one of his last prophecies, the intuitive genius, who was so fond of wearing berets, predicted that the next fantastic scientific breakthrough might be a successful antigravity device, so that man could break free of the brute force that had been keeping him glued to the earth and its near environs for so long. This event would mean that man could dispense with the need for massive rockets in order to ascend into space.

Charles E. Yeager
First Man to Fly Faster than Sound

To a rugged, stocky, ex-World War II American fighter pilot went the honor of being the first human ever to exceed the speed of sound in the sky. It took a rather unconventional rocket plane to help him accomplish this task that many cynics had predicted couldn't be done. Fortunately, several visionaries had faith that this heretofore unattainable goal — of crossing the mysterious, unseen barrier in the atmosphere — could be achieved before the 20th century reached its half-way mark.

When Captain Charles "Chuck" Yeager of the U.S. Air Force and his family arrived at Muroc Dry Lake in the Mojave Desert of California in the late 1940's, they found an infant air base operating under literally combat conditions. They were given quarters in an inconvenient, poorly lighted barracks. Military and civilian workers at the base lived in abandoned mineshafts, shacks, Quonset huts, and trailers.

On the flight line where the X–1 was being checked out, the temperatures climbed anywhere from 118 to 150 degrees F. during the summer. During the winter nights, the temperatures plummeted down well below freezing. In the afternoons, strong winds blew dust and sand over the landscape which stung the face of anyone who ventured outdoors during one of the periodic sandstorms.

But somehow during the summer and early fall of 1947, the maintenance crew from Bell Aircraft, who built the X–1, and the Air Force technicians managed to overcome the elements and get the cigar-shaped little rocket plane ready for its historic flight into near space.

On October 14, 1947, the sun peeped over Lonely Peak in the Sierra Nevada mountains to bathe the desolate dry lake in a warm orange glow which matched the color of the rocket plane. On this day, Yeager's tiny plane was nestled in the bomb bay of a giant B–29 Air Force bomber which had been specially fitted to carry him aloft; serving as the mothership in the operation. The two planes had been mated and fueled shortly before. The liquid oxygen, which provided the oxidizer to keep the alcohol burning at high altitudes, had by now formed a frosty coating around the main body of his plane. The excess LOX, which was fuming off from its escape valve, presented an eerie, science fiction sight to the casual onlooker witnessing the operation. Since liquid oxygen is formed at the low temperature of minus 297 degrees Fahrenheit, it boils off in a white vapor when it comes into contact with the air.

Just after dawn, Chuck Yeager climbed into the B–29 carrying his clipped wing rocket ship, named the *Glamorous Glennis,* after his wife, and prepared to try to do what no man had ever accomplished before — fly faster than sound. No one knew if the sonic barrier could be pierced successfully by a man-made object. Many pessimistic aeronautical engineers had speculated that the high G forces and resulting shock waves would tear any missile or aircraft apart and kill its occupant. But Yeager was willing to try and see if he couldn't penetrate this heretofore unconquered barrier and survive.

Yeager made sure his high altitude pressure suit and instruments were all working properly before he gave the signal to his ground and B–29 crews that he was ready to go. While the converted bomber was revving up its four propeller-driven engines, preparatory to its takeoff roll with its precious cargo slung under its belly, the F–80 Shooting Star and P–51 Mustang chase planes left the ground and began circling overhead, waiting for the lumbering bomber to climb up and meet them. Inside the bomber, Yeager was helped by the crew chief to tighten the laces on the legs of his pressure suit before descending into the cockpit of the X–1. He had difficulty squirming into the harness of his parachute pack, but he finally made it into his gear.

As the struggling B–29 reached an altitude of 8,000 feet, Chuck prepared to squirm down into the crowded cockpit of the *Glamorous Glennis*. The project engineer waved a good luck sign to Chuck as he slipped down inside the open bomb bay. He had to actually climb outside the Super Fortress to get inside his plane, dangling by a few clamps to the bomber's innards. A metal shield had been placed in the front of the bomb bay outside the plane to protect Chuck from being blown away by the violent wind blasts as he transferred from the larger to the smaller vehicle. After checking all his instruments, he called up to the B–29, via his radio headset, that all was in order for the launch.

He received one more request from the launch control panel crewman in the mothership to increase the nitrogen pressure in his fuel tank some 25 pounds per

The Bell X–1 rocket plane, first aircraft to fly faster than the speed of sound. Capt. Yeager named the bullet-like plane "Glamorous Glennis" after his wife.

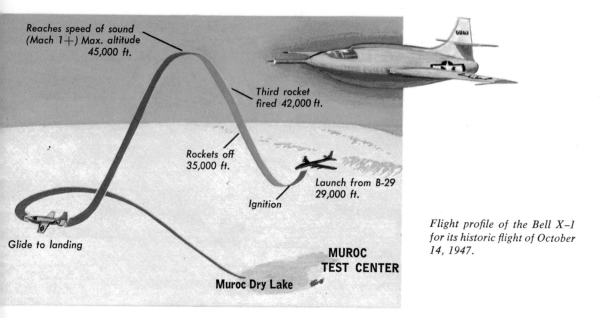

Reaches speed of sound (Mach 1+) Max. altitude 45,000 ft.

Third rocket fired 42,000 ft.

Rockets off 35,000 ft.

Launch from B-29 29,000 ft.

Ignition

Glide to landing

Muroc Dry Lake

MUROC TEST CENTER

Flight profile of the Bell X–1 for its historic flight of October 14, 1947.

square inch. They were now at 29,000 feet and some 45 minutes after take-off. It was a bare six minutes to drop time. The chase planes were banking and swerving about the mothership like birds at play, waiting for the drop to occur.

One of the chase planes flew close by to check the blue-white LOX vapor streaming from the vent valves in the amber-colored rocket plane's belly. It reported to Yeager that all was well as the pilot observed the steady bleed of excess LOX from the jettison tube of his hummingbird.

Chuck then heard a voice from the B–29 ask: "All clear to drop?"

"All clear," he called back curtly.

"Here comes the final countdown," said the voice of the project engineer after informing the Captain that the drop cameras had been turned on.

From this moment on, Yeager was all alone. He could no longer cut in his radio to abort the mission.

"Five seconds," called the engineer at the console in the B–29, "Fo-ah, Thur-ee, Too-wuh, Wu-un, DROP!"

Simultaneously with this last staccato bark, a handle was pulled in the mothership

and the hydraulic grips released the *Glamourous Glennis* from its protective lair half inside the four-engined silver B–29.

This marked the moment of birth for the X–1. Still without power, the tiny plane glided down and away from the big converted bomber which began to circle back toward the base in the desert. Then Yeager flipped on his four rocket engine ignition switches in rapid succession. As the engines fired, the surge forward threw him back against his seat. As the fourth rocket fired, he directed the pointed nose of his X–1 upwards, climbing swiftly without a tremor to the peak of his giant arched trajectory. He couldn't hear the high supersonic whine nor see the rose-pink contrail that he left behind in the clear indigo blue heavens high above the California desert.

He was still climbing as his machmeter crawled up to .88 — where it wavered momentarily — indicating that he was traveling at nine-tenths the speed of sound. What would happen when he hit Mach 1? Would his plane hold together or disintegrate? It would not be long now before he and the chase planes found out the answer to this question. His altimeter read 42,000 feet and he knew he was already higher than the peak of Mt. Everest by some 12,000 feet.

Now his plane began to buffet violently. Gravity was trying to pull him back to earth while the rockets continued to jolt him ahead. Yeager had difficulty with his controls and he began to feel heavy and listless. The half-fogged window of his oxygen mask was beginning to trouble him and his teeth started to chatter from the shocks of the bumps as the X–1 strained to plow through the invisible wall of air that marked the unknown sound barrier. Yeager cut in his third rocket tube once again, and watched apprehensively as the machmeter gradually moved up to .98.

In a moment he would know — for the first time in history — what it would be like to plunge through the sonic barrier. While the needle fluctuated back and forth across Mach .98 for what seemed to be forever, Yeager got ready to cut in the fourth rocket tube again. Then the needle dipped suddenly and went completely off scale. He waited for disintegration of his plane and a blackout but nothing happened. Instead, his flight suddenly became smoother and control of his craft came easier. He was soon aware of an awesome silence, with all sound behind him. Yeager was actually moving well ahead of all sound now. He had successfully passed Mach 1!

Elated, Captain Yeager suppressed his joyous emotion and quickly made some mental notes of the bucking that he experienced in the transonic region. By now he was plunging down on the return slope of his roller coaster ride. The swift descent to the warmer strata of the lower atmosphere from the extremely cold higher areas had caused frost to form on his canopy. He was flying blind.

Although he couldn't see, he guided his rocketplane without power down to a lower altitude where the two white-gulled jet and piston powered chase planes picked up the descending hummingbird and talked it on down to a safe landing. The frosty ring around the X–1's belly had disappeared by now, so this absence of any residual LOX marked a welcome sign that he would not have to worry about during his landing. His canopy, unfortunately, remained fogged over with frost. But, thanks to his chase plane pilots, Yeager was directed accurately to bank and turn until he was lined up with the Muroc runway. They even told him when to lower his flaps and landing gear and counted down the last few thousand feet with him as he approached the ground.

Exactly fourteen minutes after he was dropped from the B–29, the wheels of the stubby X–1 touched the arid desert. Yeager was home again after having proved that in the future, the sonic wall of the atmosphere could never again stop man as he struggled to escape his natural birth- and nesting-place, the blue-planet Earth. After his successful flight, Yeager rose up through the ranks to become a full colonel in the Air Force and the Commander of the Air Force Flight Test Center at Edwards Air Force Base (formerly Muroc Air Force Base).

Today the orange-colored *Glamorous Glennis* hangs proudly in the Smithsonian Institution in Washington, as a historic memento of man's first successful attempt to penetrate and conquer another stubborn natural barrier — once thought to be impassable — on his quest for the stars.

"Chuck" Yeager now directs pilot training for more advanced rocket planes such as the X–15.

John P. Stapp
Explorer of the Limits of Human Endurance

Alamogordo, New Mexico, has been marked in history as the place where the first atomic bomb was built and tested. Nine years after that cataclysmic, earth-shaking event lit up the desert sky, another dramatic event occurred near the same town. That, too, provided a giant leap forward into the space age.

There was no mushroom cloud and ball of fire to mark this newest event, but rather the sound of rocket motors and a spray of water coming from the creation of a mild-mannered Air Force officer who wore gold-rimmed glasses. Lt. Col. John Paul Stapp of the U.S. Air Force was a dedicated medical and research scientist who had volunteered to be his own guinea pig in a strange and risky experiment to prove that man could travel near the speed of sound and then survive high G-forces while stopping suddenly, in one second flat.

He had long been obsessed with the unknown limits of physical tolerance that would permit a pilot or an astronaut to bail out safely from a jet or rocket plane's ejection seat at supersonic speeds. So, he designed a rocket-powered sled that would hurtle down a 3,500-foot-long track, making a sudden stop at the end. Stapp wanted to simulate the blast intensities and gravity pressures on the ground that a typical pilot might encounter when bailing out of a high speed plane at 35,000 feet and traveling at 1,000 m.p.h.

As a side bonus, he hoped to discover safe methods of propelling men up to earth escape velocity speeds of 25,000 m.p.h. and then to decelerate them safely on simulated re-entry runs to test the physical endurance of astronauts to the extreme rigors of space flight.

Stapp had been assigned to the Air Force Research and Development Center at Holloman Air Force Base near Alamogordo to head up their infant Aero-Medical Labora-

tory, after having conducted rocket sled tests at Muroc Dry Lake in California.

Now, on the cold morning of December 10, 1954, Stapp was preparing to travel at or near the speed of sound on land for the first time. His new vehicle carried nine JATO (Jet Assisted Takeoff) rocket bottles attached to the back of his sled, generating a total of over 40,000 pounds of thrust. He estimated that when he reached top speed, his little sled would be developing about 70,000 horsepower, which would give him a fantastic push as he whizzed along the track.

Stapp wasn't sure how his body would withstand this latest test. Just nine months before he had traveled at 421 m.p.h. on a smaller sled, surviving 22 G's for a full second. But this time things would be different, and he wondered just how many G-weights he could pull and survive (the body normally pulls one G at sea level doing regular routines). He knew he would be exposing himself to a dangerously high rate of deceleration at the end of the run.

On this day he was out to prove the

truth of his personal proverb which was neatly lettered on a large placard placed on his office desk back at the base headquarters. It read: DON'T BE MISLED BY KAKORRHAPHIOPHOBIA INTO OSPHRESIOLAGNIA. In lay language, this confusing phrase could be freely translated to mean: "Don't be misled by an exaggerated fear of failure into believing that everything stinks." Stapp, the quiet, little bachelor-medico had no fear of failure.

Stapp was actually a rarity in the Air Force (and in the civilian world as well), for he actually possessed a double doctorate; one in medicine and a Ph.D. in biophysics. He had spent fourteen years working his way through various universities and somehow managing to pay for the education of several younger brothers at the same time.

Now, in his late forties, Stapp had kept his vow, that he would be the first man to conduct any new experiment that he designed for his rocket sled before risking the life of others. This obsession stemmed from two shocking incidents which had occurred in his youth: the fatal burning of an infant cousin and the death in an auto accident of a girl whom he was engaged to marry. His perplexity over their deaths from shock caused him to change the whole course of his life and to enter medicine.

At Muroc, Stapp analyzed the impact forces of rapid deceleration using laboratory animals (including bears) on some 90 sled runs. He found that safe tolerance to high G forces or sudden impact could be achieved by use of a restraining harness. He concluded that if people in autos could be strapped in their seats in similar fashion, they could probably survive most accidents; but the auto industry was not ready to take his advice for several years. In 1952, for his work at Muroc, the Air Force had presented Stapp with the Legion of Merit, one of its highest honors.

On this fateful day in December 1954 Stapp was probing the very limits of human

Assistants at Holloman Air Force Base strap Colonel Stapp to his 2,000-pound sled.

endurance. He was assisted by Major David Simons, another Air Force M.D., who was to achieve fame in his own right a few years later as the first man to soar over 100,000 feet in a balloon — and live. While the Major was preparing to give him a check with a mercury manometer, Stapp quipped, "I can tell you in advance, Dave, that my blood pressure is high; my pulse is also fast due to an excessively rapid heartbeat caused by the adrenaline of anxiety being pumped into the heart at an abnormal rate."

Together, they drove out in Simons' car, past the guards to the sled-site bordering on the New Mexico dunes of powdered gypsum that flanked the edge of White Sands National Monument. They soon came upon a half-dozen men working over two strange cars sitting on one end of the three-fifths-mile-long track. One car held a shoebox-like structure. About two-thirds of the way back from its squared-off edge was a steel chair on which Stapp would be strapped for his experiment. Two high speed motion picture cameras were mounted on the front of the sled, facing back toward the seat, so that photographs could be taken of the occupant during the experiment.

Behind this first sled, rested a second one carrying the rockets and more cameras to photograph the water brake systems that would slow the sled down at the end of the track in a split second. Each sled was fitted with curved water scoops underneath that

Colonel Stapp's railed sled plows a geyser of water in coming to a quick stop.

would bring the tandem sleds to a halt when they passed over a water-filled canal at the end of the run. After checking his instruments and the JATO rockets with the Northrup engineers who designed the sled, Stapp climbed aboard and was strapped into his replica of an aircraft pilot's seat.

Someone had painted "Sonic Wind No. 1" on his 15-foot-long, 2,000-pound, queer-looking contraption, that did not look as if it could ever attain supersonic speeds. It was not streamlined, but looked more like something out of a Hollywood horror movie. But Stapp was happy when he climbed aboard his invention. "After all, I can rejoice when I get up there," he quipped to his crew, "because there are no telephones aboard."

Stapp and his project engineer were finally satisfied that all was in readiness, including the water level at the end of the run. Now, the little Colonel was strapped, facing forward, into the sled. Multiple safety belts were adjusted with the help of four assistants. One of them shoved a black gum rubber mouthpiece between his lips to prevent him from biting his tongue or fracturing any teeth. Another pulled a specially designed crash helmet down over his head, while a third strapped his knees and ankles firmly to the metal chair base.

By the time they were finished, the countdown had reached X —35 minutes and the morning sun had crept up over the Organ Mountains in the distance. A siren wailed, and two warning flares arced up into the sky. It was X —5 minutes, and Major Simons and Sgt. Jim Ferguson dashed away, leaving Stapp to face the ordeal of the experiment, helplessly alone. He knew he would soon become a human test-bed, catapulting forward into the unknown forces of nature. Could he withstand them and live? He sat like a deaf mute as the countdown neared zero, tensing his body for the shock that would soon come from behind him. Everything was still, except for the faint voice of the control-panel operator, in the blockhouse, ticking off the final ten seconds of the countdown: "X minus 10 seconds...9...8...7...6 ...5...4...3...2...1. Fire."

As the switch slammed shut, a volcanic blast of smoke and orange flame belched out of the rear of Stapp's strange-looking contraption. The two sleds shot forward as if they had been hurled from a cannon. The first surge of rocket power had slammed his chair against his back. Slowly, he felt the increasing pressure of the wind and G-pressure crunching his body, muscles, and brain. He could not breathe. Although

Stapp knew that some blood remained in his brain, he could hardly see because of the loss of blood from his eyes. He had accelerated to a peak speed of 632 m.p.h. in five-seconds time, while traveling a distance of 2,800 feet.

As he approached the water braking area and the rockets ceased firing, Stapp became aware that everything had suddenly exploded in front of him in a lacework of vivid colors and pain. A giant sledgehammer swung into his back and his eyeballs snapped forward. He thought they might even leave their sockets, and be torn from his body. Simultaneously, his lungs were compressed as he was jammed tighter and tighter against his chest straps. While slowing down during the one and a half seconds of sharp braking, Stapp withstood a deceleration equal to 35 times the force of gravity and a wind pressure of more than two tons.

After the sled stopped, he realized that the pain in his eyes was still intense. "I can't see," he thought, with a sudden twinge of fear, as the color before him changed from a bright red to a warm pinkish brown. He fought to stay conscious as a sudden mood of discouragement overtook him. "I can't see," he muttered over and over. In his stupor, he wondered if the force of gravity experienced by the sharp deceleration had pulled his eyeballs far enough out of shape to tear away the retinas and blind him for the rest of his life.

The four men who were sprinting madly toward his sled did not know of his agony. The giant spray of water that had stopped him in the nick of time had subsided now, so that welcome hands could get to him and loosen the straps that held him tightly bound to the sled.

When Simons and the others arrived, they were shocked to discover that the face on the limp figure was blue from anoxia — caused by the choking off of his oxygen supply during the buffeting that he took near the end of the run. Stapp's hands and feet were chilled with cold. He also was in a state of shock. "You certainly have a beautiful pair of shiners, John," said Simons, not knowing that Stapp could not see. They placed him gently on a stretcher and carried him over to a nearby ambulance. After checking his heart and pulse rate, they determined that Stapp was now returning to near normal. Hopefully, the sledrider noticed that small flecks of blue were beginning to creep over the pinkish brown blur of his vision. With his fingers, he pushed back his eyelids but still could not make out any objects. Twenty minutes later when the ambulance arrived at the base hospital, a grateful Stapp was lifted out and he noticed for the first time that the blue flecks above him were part of the sky. He was not blind after all. "When the pieces of sky coalesced and stuck together into a constant visual field," he said later, "I began to feel relief and a wondrous elation. The lights were turned back on again. I could see!"

He had traveled over nine-tenths of the speed of sound on land and lived to tell about his experiences. His test led the way to designing safer, crash-proof seats and safety harnesses for astronauts and high altitude test pilots.

Soon after his historic feat, Stapp was made a full Colonel. He married and went on to become Chief of the Aero-Medical Laboratory of the Wright Air Development Center in Ohio, where he pioneered many other medical experiments, to help make man's plunge into space less hazardous. A grateful American Rocket Society honored this quiet man of stubborn initiative a few years later with its Presidency.

Colonel Stapp's face shows the stresses endured on high speed test run.

Wernher von Braun

Builder of America's Rockets for the Space Race

When October 4, 1957 ushered in the birth of the Space Age with the orbiting of the first Soviet Sputnik, a German-American rocket engineer at Redstone Arsenal in Huntsville, Ala., felt a deep pang of remorse. As the chief of development of the Army Ballistic Missile Agency, Dr. Wernher von Braun had been pleading, in vain, with his superiors for the privilege of trying to put the free world's first artificial satellite into orbit around the earth but he had always been rebuffed.

Years earlier, as a youth in Berlin, he had helped to build and fly homemade rockets on a municipal dump, and ever since those adventurous days back in the thirties, he had dreamed of designing bigger and better rockets, predicting that one day . . ."space travel will free man from his remaining chains, the chains of gravity which still tie him to this planet. It will then open to him the gates of heaven."

Now, however, he had to suffer with his adopted nation as the Russians basked in their newly won prestige in the wake of the technological success of Sputnik 1. Von Braun had been attending a Redstone dinner honoring Secretary of Defense Neil McElroy on the night the first Sputnik was sent into orbit. After breaking the shocking news to those assembled, von Braun addressed the Pentagon chief: "Sir," he said earnestly, "when you get back to Washington you'll find that all hell has broken loose. I wish you would keep one thought in mind through all the noise and confusion: we can fire a satellite into orbit 60 days from the moment you give us the green light!"

Army Secretary Wilber Brucker, who had accompanied McElroy, the ex-soap executive, raised a hand in objection: "Not 60 days." Although von Braun was insistent that he could accomplish the feat in two months, his boss, General John Medaris settled it: "Ninety days." A month later the second Sputnik, with the dog Laika aboard, soared into space. McElroy remembered the Army's promise and called down to Medaris at Huntsville and gave his approval for the Army to move ahead on its satellite project. Medaris called to von Braun immediately over his Redstone squawkbox with the command: "Wernher, let's go!"

With the Navy's three-stage Vanguard satellite launching rocket being plagued with troubles, the go-ahead to the Army came none too soon for the United States. One of von Braun's first actions was to reserve the Cape Canaveral range for the night of January 29, 1958 between 10:30 P.M. and 2:30 A.M. (he would have hit his planned target date right on the nose except for bad weather). His Jupiter–C (a modified Redstone rocket) had been ready for months. "All she needed was a good dusting," he said, as he worked his staff to rig together with baling wire a small 22-pound tubular satellite to put on top of the rocket.

This Explorer 1 satellite, which had been constructed by Dr. William Pickering and his staff at the Jet Propulsion Laboratory in co-operation with Dr. James Van Allen of the State University of Iowa, was the result of "silent coordination" among the three men over a period of several months. Thus, on January 31, 1958, just 84 days after being given the go-ahead by McElroy, Explorer 1 streaked into orbit to regain for the United States an important leg in the race into space.

During World War II, at the youthful age of 32, von Braun was put in charge of the top-secret German rocket base at Peenemünde, where he proceeded to construct the deadly V-2 rocket. Patterned after ideas "borrowed" from Dr. Goddard, von Braun built imitations of the American's rockets powered by the same alcohol and liquid oxygen fuel. Between June 1942 and February 1945, some 264 V-2 rockets were test-fired, many of them reaching London. Before the war was over, some 3550 of these rockets were launched operationally at Britain, of which nearly 3000 reached their target. As Hitler's "vengeance weapon," these missiles came too late to turn the tide of the war, but they left behind a legacy of a terrifying spectacle of what World War III might be like.

In the waning days of the war, as the Allies marched into Germany, von Braun and over 130 of his top rocket engineers fled from Peenemünde to the relatively safe confines of the Harz Mountains with several truckloads of secret documents and rocket blueprints that were eventually hidden in an abandoned mine. These men were torn between surrendering to the Russians and the West, who would certainly be sympathetic with their work, and aiding the Americans in winning the war.

Their unrealistic goal was to retreat to some place where they could continue work on their rocket. Toward the end of the long winter, they finally abandoned thoughts of continuing their project and surrendered to the Americans who were advancing nearby. This seemed to them the wisest course to follow. They were soon smuggled out of Germany by General Holger Toftoy of the U.S. Army under the now famous "Operation Paperclip." Transferred as "wards of the Army," to Fort Bliss, Texas, and White Sands, New Mexico, von Braun and 133 of his men were put to work assembling and test-firing several captured German V-2 missiles during the late forties and early fifties. The launching of a WAC-Corporal rocket atop a V-2 established a high altitude record of 250 miles, a record which stood for many years.

Most of the German team liked America, sent for their families and, eventually, became naturalized American citizens. In the early fifties, von Braun found himself transferred, with his still loyal crew, to the Army Ballistic Missile Agency in the sleepy northern Alabama town of Huntsville. Dur-

Launching of V-2 with Wac-Corporal rocket.

ing this period, he wrote several magazine articles pleading with America, his adopted country, to wake up to the possibilities of space flight.

He was bitterly disappointed when his Project Orbiter proposal, to put an artificial earth satellite into orbit around the earth, was shelved by the White House in 1955 in favor of the Navy's Project Vanguard. The reason given by the Government's decision makers: the U.S. wanted to use a "peaceful" (but untried) scientific rocket instead of the "military"-oriented Redstone missile which von Braun had built for the Army and successfully test-fired at Cape Canaveral as early as 1953.

When von Braun was told by the scientists that the Vanguard rocket had more "dignity," he snorted: "Dignity! I'm all for dignity. But this instrument is a cold-war tool. How dignified would our position

Lift-off of Jupiter–C rocket and Explorer 1.

really be if a man-made star of unknown origin suddenly appeared in our skies?" He and his rocket team were specifically ordered to forget about satellite work and concentrate instead on developing the Army's Jupiter intermediate range missile as a competitor to the Air Force's Thor. To achieve this end, von Braun told his superiors that he needed some test vehicles to iron out some of the problems which had cropped up in the development of the new rocket. So he wangled permission to build 12 Jupiter–C rockets, which were actually almost the same as the improved Redstone, with the addition of some solid fueled upper stages which he had previously proposed to use in putting a small satellite into orbit.

By September 20, 1956, the first Jupiter–C was ready for firing at Cape Canaveral. It was a four-stage missile with a dummy satellite fourth stage. But the Pentagon brass, who had a notion that von Braun might be trying to beat the Navy into space with an unauthorized and "undignified" satellite, brought pressure on the Army to prevent him from making a live launching. Although such Army Generals as Medaris and James Gavin, the chief of Research and Development, foresaw a successful Army satellite launching and its rocket superiority as a splendid opportunity for their branch of the service to make a name for itself, they and von Braun were to be denied the immediate chance to prove out their vehicle's worth.

Medaris had no choice but to call von Braun: "Wernher," he said glumly, "I must put you under direct orders personally to inspect that fourth stage to make sure it is not live." Without the satellite (which von Braun kept locked up in a closet at Huntsville), the Jupiter–C flew 3300 miles downrange — farther than any American — or Russian — missile had flown at that time. The success of this flight, however, gave von Braun the feeling that he could surely launch a satellite into orbit around the earth, if only given the chance.

As everyone knows, he got that chance just over a year later. Von Braun richly deserved the accolades that came his way along with those heaped upon Drs. Pickering and Van Allen. On the night of January 31, 1958, after they had received the news that their offspring had gone into orbit, the three men stood in the Great Hall of the National Academy of Sciences and proudly held aloft a dummy Explorer satellite.

When the National Aeronautics and Space Administration was born in mid–1958, von Braun and his team, which had grown to over 3300 scientists and technicians, were transferred from Army control to the space agency's jurisdiction. Their facility was renamed the Marshall Space Flight Center after the World War II general and von Braun was soon given new and complicated tasks to perform. He was put in charge of developing the giant Saturn boosters which will loft our astronauts to the moon in their Apollo spacecraft, hopefully, sometime near the end of this decade.

So far, he has successfully test-fired over a half dozen of these giant rockets which are many times larger and more powerful than the Model T Jupiter–Cs and Redstones. Today, von Braun struggles on to help see that America does not finish second in the moon race. In an interview, with his devoted wife and two daughters spurring him on, von Braun has this to say about his adopted country:

. . ."America has really been nice to us, and although we had to sit around and see the U.S. make some of the mistakes we had made long ago in missilery — it was like coming around the same track again — and we did feel frustrated at times, we are awfully lucky to have carried the day. It makes us feel that we paid back a part of a debt of gratitude we owed this country. . . .

"You know, some think of the earth as a safe and comfortable planet, and they say that space is a hostile environment. This is not really true. Earth is protected by its blanket of atmosphere, to be sure, but it is

The giant Saturn V rocket developed by von Braun will take Apollo astronauts to the moon.

a disorderly place, and unpredictable. It is full of storms and winds, of fogs and ice, or earthquakes. It is also full of people — people with thermonuclear bombs.

"There is a beauty in space, and it is orderly. There is no weather, and there is regularity. It is predictable. Just look at our little Explorer; you can set your clock by it — literally; it is more accurate than your clock. Everything in space obeys the laws of physics. If you know these laws, and obey them, space will treat you kindly. Don't tell me Man doesn't belong out there. Man belong wherever he wants to go — and he'll do plenty well when he gets there."

This is the vision of America's foremost rocket engineer and popular Space Age prophet — the vision of one who has achieved a remarkable series of successes both for himself and his adopted country, as we plunge ever deeper into the cosmos.

John R. Pierce

Builder of the First Communications Satellite

In the October 3, 1945, issue of an obscure journal called *Wireless World*, a then little known British science fiction writer, Arthur Clarke, wrote an article entitled: "Extraterrestrial Relays." As the first man to propose the feasibility of communications satellites, some dozen years before the Space Age was born, Clarke envisioned three stationary comsats circling in space at a 22,300 mile altitude and covering the earth with their radio, TV, and telephonic messages. He predicted the synchronous-type communications satellites which are relaying TV pictures across the oceans on a regular operational basis today.

Before these present space relay devices were sent into the cosmos, a huge passive balloon satellite was hurled into orbit as a Model–T forerunner of the more sophisticated, active comsats now constructed. This pioneer communications satellite was properly named "Echo" and the man who spearheaded the project for the Bell Telephone Labs and NASA was a research scientist named John R. Pierce.

John Pierce was born at Clear Lake, Iowa, and gave early signs that he was an extraordinary child. Though consistently earning grades that led his class, young Pierce was never able to stay in school through an entire term. He had undergone a major operation when he was only one day old, and he was so plagued with subsequent illnesses, such as scarlet fever and nephritis, during his early years that his mother once jokingly said to her sister: "Why couldn't we exchange some of John's brain for some of your children's brawn?"

At the age of thirteen, young Pierce was taken by his parents to California where it was hoped that the milder climate would aid his struggle to regain his health. There, beneath a palm tree in the courtyard of the Redlands Public Library, he discovered the world of H. G. Wells. "I was just over-whelmed by *The Time Machine*," he said later, "so I read a lot of his novels. Wells had great insight. He saw that science was changing the world. He underestimated the task — it seemed easier to him than it actually is. But his vision that science could effect this change was what fascinated me."

While still an adolescent, Pierce learned that some things are possible and others are not. This wisdom came from experience when he acquired a passionate interest in gliders. With two high school friends, Oliver La Rue and Apollo Smith, he tried to construct the first dual-control glider — utilizing more enthusiasm than skill.

Upon completion of high school, he entered Cal Tech in a small, hand-picked class. He worked on the school paper where he improved his facility in writing (which is one skill many scientists lack). One of his classmates was Simon Ramo, who later went on to found a multi-million dollar electronics firm advising the Air Force on their ballistic missile program.

Still not sure of a career, Pierce went on to do graduate work at Cal Tech since he could not find a job after receiving his bachelor's degree. Pierce helped to finance his graduate courses through laboratory work and the sale of his writings. He even saved up enough to take a trip to Europe, departing just before the commencement exercises were held at which he was to be awarded his Ph.D.

Upon his return to New York from Europe, he happily discovered that a position was awaiting him at the Bell Labs through the intercession of one of his Cal Tech professors. He went to Murray Hill, N. J., where the Labs are located on a picturesque hillside, and has remained there ever since.

"Though I had a doctor's degree, I still didn't know what it was all about when I came to Bell," he relates. "I was told to do research. It took me a long time to find out what this meant. Mostly I had to learn to do research by myself, which wasn't a good way. . . . You have to learn by example, like learning to play a game."

He stressed a vital point on this phase of his career: "In research, you never find quite what you set out to find, so you must be aware of what you do find!"

It was not a fluke that Pierce should become aware of Arthur Clarke's prophecy since he had been a science-fiction buff for a long time. He had himself published eight science-fiction articles under the pseudonym of J. J. Coupling as well as some twenty popular science pieces, in addition to his dozens of learned academic papers.

In the March 1952 issue of *Astounding Science-Fiction,* Pierce had set his mind on communications when he wrote under the Coupling by-line: "The truth is that you could order equipment for an earth-moon link from any of several manufacturers. The plain truth is that any communications engineer would give his eyeteeth to have the cheap and easy earth-moon path to span rather than the tough coast-to-coast path."

What he was referring to, of course, was the problem of relaying television pictures over the curvature of the earth from point-to-point. The use of coaxial cables and properly spaced relay towers eliminated this problem over the land areas, but relaying the same signal over the oceans was another matter. It would be too expensive to place a dozen or more Texas Tower floating radar islands in the Atlantic or Pacific to link up the continents with live TV.

Pierce, in his capacity as a leading researcher for the world's largest communications enterprise, the American Telephone and Telegraph Co., saw an opportunity to extend his knowledge to the space medium. Bell had already successfully perfected microwave techniques after World War II to make possible the transmission of long distance phone calls across the continent. This wireless means of communication was later adopted for TV transmission and relay but was limited to overland use.

In 1954, three years before Sputnik, Pierce wrote an article in *Jet Propulsion,* the Journal of the American Rocket Society, about a simple sort of communications satellite. He proposed the idea of using a 100-foot-diameter balloon to be made of aluminum foil. By 1958 the Space Age was well under way. In that year Pierce attended a secret meeting of space scientists at Woods Hole, Massachusetts.

The Cape Cod meeting brought together members of the National Research Council

Echo 1, 100-foot space mirror undergoes test.

and the National Academy of Sciences to seek military solutions for the Air Force to the problem of satellite communications and other matters. Pierce and his associate, Dr. Rudolph Kompfner, who is now Director of Radio and Electronics Research at the Bell Labs, knew of the existence of suitable equipment to make a pioneering experiment in space communications. NASA's Langley Field research team had just built a 100-foot-wide aluminum-coated Mylar balloon which was to be launched into a 1,000 mile-high orbit to measure the air density drag at that height.

Pierce realized the possibility of combining two experiments in one launching; so he and Kompfner discussed their plan with Dr. William Pickering, the Director of NASA's Jet Propulsion Laboratory at Cal Tech. Pickering approved of the idea and suggested that JPL's ground tracking facilities at Goldstone, California, be used as one end of the communications link in the nation-spanning earth-to-space-to-earth operation. Pickering also suggested that the Bell Labs provide the other end of the link somewhere on the east coast. And so, Project Echo was born.

But before the balloon could be launched for the experiment, an elaborate receiving ear antenna had to be constructed at a cost of about half a million dollars. After a period of uncertainty, during which the Bell Labs asked themselves if this were really a good thing, construction was finally started at Holmdel, New Jersey.

When the horn listening device was completed, with its sensitive ruby maser eardrum, a Thor–Delta rocket was readied at Cape Canaveral to launch the folded Echo into orbit where it would be inflated. On August 12, 1960, after a normal countdown, the Echo was placed into a near perfect orbit. About two minutes after the payload was injected into orbit, the outside container was separated by an explosive charge. Special powders which changed into gas in the near-vacuum of space inflated the balloon and it was ready to reflect signals from earth. Man's first passive communications satellite had been put into space and John Pierce's dreams had been brought to a reality.

The first "official" message bounced off the shiny silvery satellite's aluminum hide as it crossed the Midwest consisted of the recorded voice of President Eisenhower. (Actually, the first real, initial pickup at Holmdel in a pre-launch test was the voice of an excited technician from Goldstone

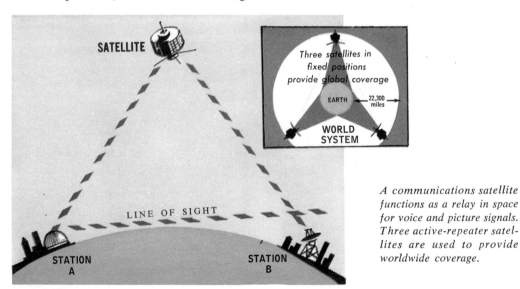

A communications satellite functions as a relay in space for voice and picture signals. Three active-repeater satellites are used to provide worldwide coverage.

asking: "Hey, Walt! Can you hear me?")

The huge sphere circled the earth every 121.6 minutes at altitudes ranging from 1,018 to 1,160 miles. For the first time, millions of people could see the satellite with their naked eyes just after sunset or before sunrise as it came across the horizon in a west-to-east direction with the sun reflecting off its shiny Mylar skin.

As Pierce put it: "The equipment we built for Echo allowed us to uncover many problems that helped us plan future communications satellites."

Echo pioneered the path for the later active communications satellites like, Telstar, Relay, Syncom, and Early Bird. More important, it set the stage for the establishment of the Communications Satellite Corporation by President Kennedy and Congress in 1962. The stock of this new multimillion dollar corporation zoomed on the Wall Street market when it was offered to the public. John Pierce's dream had overnight evolved into a major new business which in time would benefit millions of people around the world with instantaneous global television, radio, telegraph and telephonic hookups from any spot on the planet.

John Pierce, the Director of Research Principles at the Bell Labs, is surrounded by electronics geniuses. But he outshines them all. His great contributions, besides the Echo and Telstar, have included major advancements made on the electron gun and the traveling wave tube. Although he did not have a direct hand in two other important Bell Lab inventions — the transistor and the solar cell, which were both essential for the operation of most satellites, he was aware of their potential to make such later communications satellites as Telstar and Relay practical.

Pierce's philosophy of life encompasses more than his profession. "If people are to be intelligent about the world," he said, "they will have to know something about science. They will have to develop some

First television transmission via Telstar.

sense of what is possible and what is not, and to get over the idea that all you have to do is appropriate a billion dollars and everything will take care of itself."

Pierce does not have a long-range future goal. "I think it is very dangerous to have ideas about 1980," he said. "If you make up your mind about what the future is going to be so far in advance, when it comes along it is very hard to get the preconception out of your mind and recognize it for what it is. What you need to know is what step to take next, and what will accomplish something the next year or the year after. You need a fairly near goal, because then you can visualize it more clearly and you can work toward it with more enthusiasm. Don't disregard the future, but make up your mind only as much as you need to in order to proceed right now, because you are foreclosing the future when you have too definite ideas."

Pierce believes that we are living in the most exciting age of man's history, but that not enough people are watching. The real excitement of each new technological advance, he feels, is not in the thing itself, but in its relation to man, because it came from man's mind. This is the real meaning of the impact of the communications satellites which are doing more to revolutionize man's communications with his fellow man than any event since Gutenberg's invention of printing with moveable type.

Alan B. Shepard Jr.

First American Into Space

There are moments in a nation's history when its hopes, fears, and confidence in its own destiny seem to be caught up in the fate of a single man. One of these rare moments occurred on the warm, sunny spring morning of May 5, 1961 when a 37-year-old naval test-pilot astronaut, Commander Alan B. Shepard Jr., climbed into his tiny Mercury capsule *Freedom 7* and prepared to become the first American to be rocketed into space.

Twice in the previous month, America had suffered two back-to-back blows to her pride with the Bay of Pigs fiasco in Cuba followed by the orbiting of the Soviet Cosmonaut Yuri Gagarin in his Vostok on April 12th. There was one significant difference between the launchings of the Russian and the American spacemen. Where the former was sent into orbit in secrecy, Shepard prepared for his historic suborbital flight in his small 2800-pound, ink bottle-shaped spacecraft under the scrutiny of some 500 news, radio and TV correspondents who had gathered at Cape Canaveral from all over the world to view the attempted launching.

As he rested atop the 70-foot tall Redstone rocket booster, waiting for the countdown to reach zero, Shepard knew that if he failed in his mission, his country would suffer a third black eye to her tarnished prestige. As the nation watched over millions of television sets or listened in on their radios, the dramatic countdown reached zero at 9:34 E.S.T. on that fateful Friday morning. One second later, the white-painted rocket ignited and slowly lifted off the pad, trailing a vertical white plume of smoke, dotted with orange flame.

In 15 minutes he made a giant arc through space, soaring to a peak altitude of 116 miles high before splashing down 302 miles out in the Atlantic. Within a few minutes after landing safely in the water under the protective cloak of his candy-striped parachute, Shepard was hoisted out of the ocean by a helicopter crew dispatched by the aircraft carrier, *Lake Champlain,* which had been sent to rescue him. "Boy what a ride," said a grateful Shepard to the whirlybird crew as they pulled him up, sans space helmet, into the protective cocoon of the hovering 'copter at 9:54 A.M.

Shepard had successfully completed the first short and cautious step into space by an American astronaut, but more important, he had given a tremendous lift to our sagging national morale in the space race in which we had too often seemed to be trailing the Red Star into orbit. The United States had staked its political prestige, technological reputation and the life of one of its highly trained, hand-picked young men on a gamble in a goldfish bowl and the results had paid off handsomely.

The nation was soon caught up in the euphoria that followed his successful, first manned mission into space. On the following Monday, the smiling, crew-cut Shepard, his wife and the other six Mercury astronauts met with the President and Mrs. Kennedy in Washington, attended a mammoth news conference, conferred with Congressmen and was the center of attention in several parades held in his honor. "All America rejoices in this successful flight of astronaut Shepard," President Kennedy declared. "This is an historic milestone in our own exploration of space . . . The flight should provide incentive to everyone in our nation concerned with this program to redouble their efforts."

All had not run smoothly, however, in the preparation for the flight. The week had begun on a dismal note for Test No. 108 at Cape Canaveral — which was the official title for the space shot. Shepard's flight had originally been scheduled for Tuesday, May 2nd, but squally weather downrange had forced an indefinite postponement after Shepard, waiting for a break in the cloud-cover, had lingered for more than three hours in his spacesuit inside his cramped Mercury capsule.

During the next three days of delay, Shepard kept busy in the secluded quarters at Hangar S on the Cape, protected from inquisitive newsmen by a high, wire fence and security guards. While waiting for the weather to clear he rehearsed again with his back-up pilot, John Glenn, his many assignments on the forthcoming flight. To break the routine of "boning up" on his flight procedures, he even managed to take some time off and go fishing and jogging along the beach, until the "go" sign that the skies were clearing was flashed by the base meteorologist.

At 10:30 P.M. on Thursday night Shepard and Glenn went to bed after a quiet evening of studying. A short two and a half hours later, at 1:05 A.M., the astronauts' personal physician, Flight Surgeon William K. Douglas, woke both men. After they each breakfasted on a 7-ounce filet mignon, wrapped in bacon, and washed down with orange juice, Douglas began the final physical checkup of both astronauts.

Ready for America's first space flight, astronaut Shepard moves toward the floodlit Redstone missile on Launch Pad 5. He carries a portable air conditioner to cool his aluminized pressure suit. Vapors streaming from poised Redstone are liquid oxygen fumes.

By 3 A.M., Shepard had been wired for his flight with four electrocardiogram (EKG) electrodes taped to his chest to measure his heartbeat, along with other medical electronic devices to measure his breathing and body temperature during the flight. It took another hour for him to struggle into his silver-coated spacesuit and clamp down the white plastic space helmet on his suit's oval neck ring.

Finally at 4 A.M., he walked into the waiting medical van, carrying his portable suit air conditioner in one hand, and was driven out to Pad #5 where his Redstone rocket and Mercury capsule were waiting for him. There was a long agonizing wait in the van until 5:15 A.M., when he stepped out into the white plumes of liquid oxygen vapor swirling about the base of the rocket. As veteran rocket crewmen and fuelers applauded, Shepard paused to eye coolly his booster for a moment and then walked into the elevator at the base of the gantry which whisked him up to his capsule perched on top of the rocket.

By 5:20 A.M., before the first faint streaks of dawn crept into the eastern sky over the nearby Atlantic, Shepard had snaked his way into the capsule and begun the final checkout. He was now awaiting the launching which had been set for 7 A.M. But one after another, last minute bugs crept into the countdown which caused the launching (T) time to be pushed back first one and then four hours. First it was a short "hold" for a weather check, then trouble in the rocket's electrical system, followed by a momentary computer failure at the Central Control Blockhouse and a faulty pressure regulator which caused further unplanned delays.

"Anything I can do to help things?" a calm Shepard asked over his intercom. Shepard was less nervous than the launch crew and doctors in the blockhouse. When lift-off finally came, two and a half hours behind schedule, the rocket rose majestically through the warm morning air on a diamond-hard tail of fire, carrying its precious human cargo into the mysterious reaches of outer space. For several seconds there was silence on the Cape and then the sound of the deep shattering roar of the rocket engine pierced the landscape.

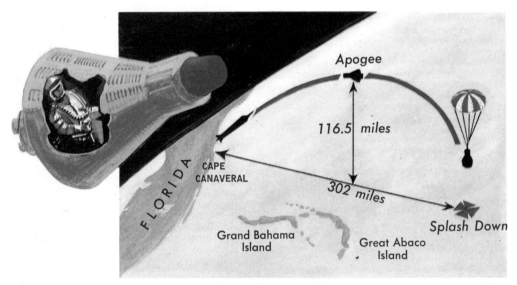

Freedom 7 capsule carries Shepard in a suborbital arc 302 miles down the Atlantic Test Range. Shepard's splashdown was only seven miles from calculated landing point off the Bahama Islands.

Next the strong, assured voice of Shepard, speaking over his intercom, was relayed over the loudspeakers at the press site. "Roger, lift-off, the clock (master timer) has started." Although he knew that his mission objectives would fall short of the one-orbit flight of Gagarin achieved just 23 days before, he knew he had the opportunity to achieve several firsts of his own compared with those of the Soviet cosmonaut. He was more of a pilot, while Gagarin was just a passenger.

As his Redstone booster thundered up toward the zenith of his planned trajectory, Shepard read off periodically the figures on the gauges and dials on his instrument panel, relaying them back to the crew in the blockhouse. At 37-miles high, just 142 seconds after lift-off, he confirmed that his rocket motor had cut off. Ten second later Shepard announced "Separation A-Okay. . . . It is a lot smoother now."

For the next few minutes, he soared free and weightless at the top of the parabolic arc. Within four minutes and 30 seconds after lift-off, he had reached his peak altitude of 116 miles. Now, traveling with his capsule blunt end forward, Shepard took a quick periscope look at the sea and land below him. "What a beautiful view!" cried America's first man in space. "I'll bet it is," answered his CapCom (Capsule Communicator) Deke Slayton.

After test-firing the retro rockets to be used on later orbital flights, there was a discomforting moment when a balky panel light failed to confirm the automatic jettisoning of the retro package. Now, slashing back through the earth's atmosphere, Shepard felt the quick buildup of G–forces from zero to 11. His conditioning in the centrifuge made the shock bearable. Cabin temperature rose to 111° F. when the blunt heat shield warmed up as it clawed through the denser air.

The drogue parachute came out on schedule at 21,000 feet and Shepard breathed a sigh of relief when he saw his 63-foot red and white main chute blossom out over his head. Told by his CapCom that his impact would be "right on the button," Shepard proceeded to get ready for the landing. With the heliocopters already converging on the impact area he knew that within a few minutes he would be plucked from the water and that his ballistic flight into space would be over. Both capsule and man were tested and proved sound. America's first step to reach the moon in this decade had been taken.

Shepard was born in East Derry, New Hampshire, on November 18, 1923. He grew up in this small town which was similar in many ways to the birthplaces of the other six original Mercury astronauts. After graduating from Admiral Farragut Academy in Toms River, N. J., he was admitted to the U.S. Naval Academy in 1940. After graduating from Annapolis in 1944 he served several naval tours finally matriculating at the Navy Test Pilot School at Patuxent, Md., in 1950. During two tours at this famous school, where he also served as an instructor, he flew most of the advanced Navy jets — from the F3H Demon to the F4D Skyray. In 1958, he attended the Naval War College at Newport, R.I.

By the time he was selected as one of our first group of astronauts in 1959 he had accumulated almost 4000 hours of flying time, half of which were in jets.

Although Shepard made no further flights in the Gemini and Apollo programs, he elected to stay with the team. Promoted to full Captain in the Navy, Shepard became the head of the astronauts' office at NASA's Manned Spacecraft Center in Houston, Texas, where he administers the myriad problems of training, helping to select, and co-ordinating the other astronauts' many activities before, during and after their spaceflights.

For Shepard, the memory of those 15 short minutes in space in May 1961, will forever remain the highlight of his career as our first authentic man-in-space hero.

Virgil I. Grissom
First Human to Go Into Space Twice

Air Force Captain Virgil "Gus" Grissom was the smallest and quietest of the original seven Mercury astronauts. Weighing only 150 pounds and standing 5-feet-seven-inches tall, the slightly bow-legged Grissom prepared to take off in his *Liberty Bell 7* capsule during the early Summer of 1961 without the fanfare which his illustrious predecessor, Navy Commander Alan Shepard, had received in his *Freedom 7* capsule. Playing back-up to America's first space man in a repeat flight of the ballistic up-and-down trajectory did not offer the glamorous challenge that his fellow astronaut faced a few months earlier.

Grissom had compiled the most jet flying time of any of the astronauts, having packed one hundred combat missions under his belt in Korea in F–86 Sabrejets to account for a major slice of this record. The bemedaled, introverted Grissom (Air Medal, DFC with Oak Leaf Cluster) had, in his typically modest fashion, once said, "The glory of being first is not everything."

The mid-July 1961 flight of Grissom was approached with routine optimism by the NASA space planners. Yet, they knew that Shepard's perfect flight was no guarantee of a repeat without some unexpected malfunction. Everyone connected with the program knew that there was an element of risk involved in the undertaking.

There were a few minor differences in the *Liberty Bell 7* and *Freedom 7* capsules. One of these involved the side escape hatch. To save weight, the NASA space engineers eliminated the cumbersome mechanical device to open and close the hatch and replaced it with small explosive bolts. Grissom's capsule also contained a 19-inch picture window to insure better visibility than Shepard's capsule had with its two small round ports.

As launch time approached on a hot July 19th, the crewcut Grissom suited up after a breakfast of steak and eggs. Then, two hours before dawn, he entered the spacecraft sitting atop the pencil slim Redstone rocket. Looming over the Atlantic Ocean that day was a threatening bank of gray-black clouds, but a small patch of stars shone overhead. After several minor holds in the countdown, *Liberty Bell* lifted off Pad Five at Cape Canaveral with the morning sun glancing off the icy coating surrounding the Redstone rocket.

The pulse of the withdrawn man from Mitchell, Indiana, inside the capsule sped up to 160 beats per minute as the rocket rose slowly on a tail of scorching flame. Grissom let his capsule communicator, Alan Shepard, know that everything was going well as the 500 observing newsmen cheered him onward from the reviewing stand. He next announced that he had just won a steak dinner bet from his CapCom, Shepard, when he shouted over the intercom, "I see a star." (Although it was broad daylight on earth, the sky was pitch-black up at the 115-mile-plus altitude where Grissom now found himself.)

After sustaining a few minutes of Zero G (weightlessness), Grissom began his capsule turnaround in space and started his re-entry descent. His retros fired perfectly, although they were not needed for this was another suborbital flight and the gravitational pull of the earth would have brought him back to a splashdown without their assist. But it was a good feeling to know that they had worked on time and had been jettisoned as programmed.

Grissom called back to Cape Canaveral Mission Control: "I feel very good"—even after announcing that his deceleration had built up to 10 G's as he reached 65,000 feet altitude. He noticed, too, that he hadn't blacked out.

After his drogue and main chutes opened, Grissom relaxed inside his capsule momentarily. Then he announced, "I'm going to open my face plate. . . . Hello, I can't get one door pin back in. I've tried and tried and can't get it back in." (These door pins enabled small wires to keep the hatch from shooting off over its full 25-foot range, thus preventing a dangerous accident or injury to recovery personnel.) Gus warned them over his intercom to stay clear of the capsule recovery door after he had made a landing.

Moments later, Grissom was relieved to hear the radio relay plane, flying under the code name *Card File 23* saying: "We are heading directly toward you," as he passed through the 3000-foot altitude level above the ocean. At this point the rescue helicopters under the code name *Hunt Club* made their first contact with *Liberty Bell 7,* telling Grissom that they were now within two miles southwest of him.

Just 15 minutes and 37 seconds after launching, *Liberty Bell 7* splashed down. There was only a mild jolt as the spacecraft struck the water. Grissom soon discovered that the capsule was lying on its side with the window covered completely with water. "There was a disconcerting gurgling noise," he said later, but a quick check showed no water entering the little vehicle. Then the spacecraft slowly righted itself and the astronaut started to prepare himself for egress from his ink bottle-shaped home.

His face plate was open and he released his helmet's oxygen outlet and harness straps which held him tight on his couch during re-entry. After disconnecting all ties with his spacecraft but the oxygen hose entering the abdominal area of the suit and the wires leading to his helmet earphones, Grissom turned his attention to the door. After releasing the restraining wires, he started to remove the cover and safety pin from the hatch. Grissom called to the *Hunt Club 1* helicopter hovering overhead:

"Give me about another five minutes here, to mark these switch positions (on the instrument panel) before I give you a call to come in and hook on." The reply came: "Roger, we are ready anytime you are."

About four minutes later, Grissom said, "O.K. Latch on, then give me a call and I'll power down (to cut the capsule's battery power off) and blow the hatch. O.K. . . . I've unplugged my suit so I'm kinda warm now."

Hunt Club 1 replied that the safety horsecollar would be down there waiting for him whenever he blew the hatch. Grissom replied, "Roger!"

But before the helicopter could lower the collar and lift the capsule partially out of the water so he could safely blow the hatch, Grissom heard the hatch explode outward with a dull thud. Grissom looked up to see blue sky outside and ocean water starting to spill over the door sill.

He quickly lifted the helmet from his head and dropped it, then reached for the right side of the instrument panel and pulled himself quickly out of the hatch. Grissom, who was the best swimmer among the original astronauts, soon found himself snarled in a line attached between the dyemarker can and the spacecraft. The realization that his *Liberty Bell* capsule was sinking and that he might be pulled down with it led the

Air Force officer to immediately free himself from its potentially fatal clutches.

Meanwhile, the first helicopter had hooked onto the capsule. Its engines were heating up badly and all three of its wheels were constantly touching the water as it struggled to lift the overloaded, waterlogged capsule. Grissom, who discovered that he was being pushed under the water by the downdraft of the helicopter's blades, found himself facing a further precarious ordeal. In the excitement of hurrying to get out of his capsule before it sank beneath him, he had forgotten to lock the oxygen inlet port at the midsection of his suit. Air was seeping out of this open port and his suit, in turn, was rapidly filling up with water, forcing him to sink deeper and to swallow big mouthfuls of saltwater.

When the second helicopter, piloted by Lt. John Teinhard of Bloomington, Illinois, lowered a sling for Gus to reach, the beleaguered astronaut commented later: "I apparently got caught in the rotowash between the two helicopters because I could not get close to the second helicopter even though I could see the co-pilot in the door with a horsecollar swinging in the water."

For several minutes, which seemed an eternity, Grissom was in extreme danger of drowning as he desperately struggled to stay afloat and reach the elusive horsecollar. The second helicopter didn't dare approach too close to him for fear of tangling its rotor blades with that of the first helicopter, still struggling to save the capsule. Gus kept disappearing regularly under the mild swells as they broke over his head and each time he swallowed more ocean water. Finally, the pilot of the first helicopter, Captain Upschulte, realizing that he could not save the million dollar capsule with its valuable cargo of film and electronic records, gave the difficult order to cut the cable. As Gus watched his spacecraft sink beside him, he realized that the material proof of his historic flight would be lost forever in the 2800 fathoms (three miles) of Atlantic Ocean beneath him.

Grissom finally reached the horsecollar, but he was in so much of a hurry to get out of the water that he put the horsecollar on backwards under his armpits. He nevertheless gave the thumbs up signal to hoist away. As soon as he was pulled inside the 'copter, he grabbed for a life preserver. "My first thought was to get on a life preserver," Gus said later, "so that if anything happened to the helicopter I wouldn't have to face another ordeal in the water."

Fortunately, Grissom's post-space trial was finally over. Nineteen minutes after he struck the water, he stepped out of the rescue 'copter onto the firm deck of the carrier, *U.S.S. Randolph,* sober and serious. The first thing he asked for before being

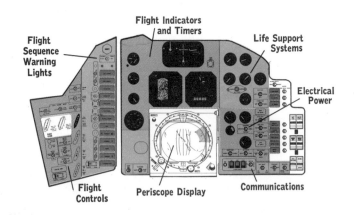

The "space dashboard" of Grissom's MR-4 spacecraft as viewed by the astronaut. The manual attitude controls for pitch, roll and yaw are at the left. Flight indicators at the center include a rotating globe which shows the capsule's position at all times. Controls at right pertain to cabin and suit conditions. The controls for other Mercury capsules were similar in design.

Flight Sequence Warning Lights

Flight Indicators and Timers

Life Support Systems

Electrical Power

Flight Controls

Periscope Display

Communications

Helicopter hooks onto water logged capsule as Grissom struggles to stay afloat.

rushed into the sick bay for a debriefing and to take a lung capacity test — was for a glass of *fresh* water.

Four years later Grissom was named the command pilot of the first Gemini flight. As a follow-on to the Mercury project, the Gemini program was established to test rendezvous and docking techniques to be used later in the Apollo three-man mission to the moon.

On March 23, 1965, Grissom and his co-pilot John W. Young were lifted into orbit by a mighty Titan II rocket. Their *Gemini 3* craft, nicknamed "the Molly Brown," completed three orbits before splashing down safely in the Atlantic Ocean. The first test of the complex maneuverable Gemini spacecraft was a success and the Gemini program was under way. Grissom had won his second set of astronaut's wings as the first human to go into space twice.

At a White House ceremony later on, President Johnson decorated both Grissom and Young with the Exceptional Service Medal, and also gave Grissom a Cluster for his NASA Distinguished Service Medal, won on his earlier Mercury flight.

But Grissom's luck ran out when he attempted to break that record and become the first man to go into space successfully on a third try. While testing the new *Apollo 1* capsule at Cape Kennedy in preparation for a two weeks orbital flight, Command Pilot Grissom, 40, and his two companions, astronauts Edward White and Roger Chaffee, were burned to death in a flash fire that ignited accidentally at 6:31 P.M. on Friday, January 27, 1967.

Grissom and Chaffee were buried a few days later in Arlington National Cemetery, near the grave of Army Lt. Thomas Selfridge, America's first airplane pilot to lose his life for his country. Grissom, who lost his life atop a Saturn moonrocket bolted to the ground at Complex 34, left his own epitaph: "If we die, we want people to accept it. The conquest of space is worth the risk of life."

John H. Glenn Jr.
America's Lindbergh of the Space Age

While Shepard's and Grissom's suborbital flights were historic space firsts, the leading national space experts on both sides of the ocean knew that the key to America's catching-up in the space race was to accomplish the much more difficult manned, orbital space flight. Russian cosmonauts, Gagarin and Titov, had successfully orbited the earth for 90 minutes and one day respectively in the spring and summer of 1961, and observers were beginning to question when America would be able to duplicate these feats. This next step forward in the state-of-the-art of rocketry was a major one well beyond putting small unmanned satellites into the cosmos or men into short duration up-and-down ballistics trajectories.

While the Soviets continued to practice secrecy about their forthcoming manned and unmanned space flights, we announced to the world that we would attempt to put up a man for three orbits late in 1961 or early 1962. Everyone knew his name, the last of the three select astronauts from the original pool of seven Mercury men. He was Lt. Colonel John Glenn, U.S.M.C., the back-up astronaut on our first flights, who was a native of Cambridge, Ohio.

Although our astronauts and space leaders were disappointed that we could not be first with this dramatic step into space, the United States announced, with White House approval, that our launch attempts would be open to both American and foreign newsmen as well as to the radio and television media. This calculated gamble meant that the whole free world could watch the final countdown and launch and thus share in the suspense of the historic moment with the astronaut and the launch crew at Cape Canaveral. Our nation's leaders knew that there was a chance that a malfunction or explosion on the launch pad could endanger the whole mission and the

life of the astronaut which would then set back our tarnished prestige still farther. But they felt that this was a risk worth taking.

For his flight Glenn had a larger booster rocket, the 360,000-pound thrust Atlas, which was a modified ICBM. In practice, unmanned test-models of this rocket functioned fairly well during the late fall of 1961, until November 10th, when a one-and-one-half-pound squirrel monkey, named Goliath, was put into a Mercury capsule as a passenger on a projected 5,000-mile downrange sub-orbital flight. But, unfortunately, fifteen seconds after launch, one of the three Atlas engines unexpectedly shut down and the other two engines were unable to keep the rocket on course. The Range Safety Officer pressed the destruct button bringing the struggling rocket, with the monkey in the capsule, to a fiery end.

Although the failure of this flight temporarily set back our plans to orbit a man, the United States was able to recoup its loss less than three weeks later when we successfully orbited a 38-pound chimpanzee, named Enos. This astroprimate made three trips around the earth before being brought safely back four-and-a-half hours later. This preview of Glenn's flight buoyed the spirits of the Mercury astronauts and their NASA team when the post-medical check showed that the space chimp had suffered no ill effects from the 56,000-mile space journey.

But the trouble that had developed with the capsule's altitude control jets during this test flight meant that it would be virtually impossible for Astronaut Glenn to attempt a manned space flight in 1961.

John Glenn was 40 years old when he prepared to ascend into space for the first time. He had been decorated many times for exploits in both World War II and Korea while flying for the Marines, receiving four DFC's and 19 Air Medals. He had flown 59 combat missions during World War II with a fighter squadron in the Marshall Islands campaign. Glenn had experienced several close calls, once collecting 300 holes in his plane and 20 in his cockpit but, miraculously, he was never scratched.

After the war, he was the first pilot, civilian or military, to fly across the United States in a jet at supersonic speed. The record flight from California to Floyd Bennett Field on Long Island took only three hours and 23 minutes.

Although Glenn had left Muskingum College in Ohio during his Junior Year (he was later awarded an honorary degree), he qualified for the Mercury program despite his lack of a college degree and his advanced age — 37. Though some believed this slightly elderly age might hamper his ability to cope with the unknown physical demands of the coming flights into space, Glenn was assigned as an alternate for one of the other candidates who had failed one of the original physical tests. His superb physical and mental condition, plus his experience, helped him to beat out most of the 501 other competitors who were seeking the seven coveted positions as our first Mercury astronaut trainees.

He suggested that his fellow astronauts take arctic, desert, and mountain survival courses to help them in case of emergency landings in those areas. This part of the training program is now routine for all new astronauts. Every day, he ran several miles to keep himself in shape and decided to live alone at NASA's training center at Langley, visiting his family at Arlington, Va., only on weekends.

The first attempts to launch Glenn's Mercury capsule, *Friendship 7,* were marred by delayed countdowns and scrubbed flights. His first orbital attempts had been delayed six times by combinations of bad weather and technical difficulties. He nearly got off the ground on Saturday, January 27, 1962, but after five hours and eleven minutes of lying on his back in the cramped capsule, that attempt was canceled because of bad weather downrange, just 20 minutes from the scheduled liftoff.

The delays couldn't go on forever. A stoical and calm Glenn decided to remain behind the gates of Cape Canaveral in his astronaut crew quarters at Hangar S — venturing out only on Sunday to attend services in the nearby Cocoa Beach Presbyterian Church. On Tuesday morning, February 20th Glenn and his back-up astronaut, Scott Carpenter, were awakened at 2:20 A.M.

Astronaut Glenn eases his way through hatch of spacecraft. The bell-shaped capsule is painted with the U.S. flag and the name "Friendship 7."

and hurriedly ate an early morning breakfast of scrambled eggs and filet mignon with Dr. William Douglas, the astronauts' personal physician, and Astronaut Major Donald "Deke" Slayton. By 4:48 A.M., he had finished the intricate dressing procedure and by 6 A.M. he walked up to the giant Atlas gantry after being transported out to the launch pad from the hangar.

This time the countdown went smoothly, and at precisely 9:47 A.M. on a cool, sunny Florida mid-winter morning, the Atlas booster lifted Glenn and his capsule gently from the pad on a column of white-hot fire and smoke. The noise was deafening on the eardrums of those watching from the press site. A tremendous crescendo of cheers arose from the 500 newsmen gathered from all over the world to watch this dramatic event. The contagion of the moment swept the crowd at the press site and on the beaches flanking the Cape which gave America a new sense of pride. In a few moments, all that was left of the mighty 85-foot-tall rocket, with its human encased in the nose, was a corkscrew contrail of

white against the blue sky. Glenn was on his way into orbit and fame.

The Atlas booster separated on schedule and the insertion into orbit was perfect. The word from Mission Control was that Glenn had a "go" for at least seven orbits, if needed. He was now traveling at 17,500 miles per hour more than a hundred miles above the earth. As he completed his first orbit, trouble developed in the automatic thrusters which control the capsule's altitude. By switching to manual control Glenn was able to stabilize his craft for the remaining orbits and, in so doing, demonstrated what man could do in controlling a vehicle in space.

The astronaut made a successful splashdown in the Atlantic Ocean at 2:43 P.M., E.S.T. but not before he and the crew at Mercury Control Center went through some tense final moments. As the capsule was completing its third orbit a false signal indicated that the heat shield was loose. Glenn was directed from the Cape to re-enter the atmosphere with his retro-package still attached to hold the heat shield in

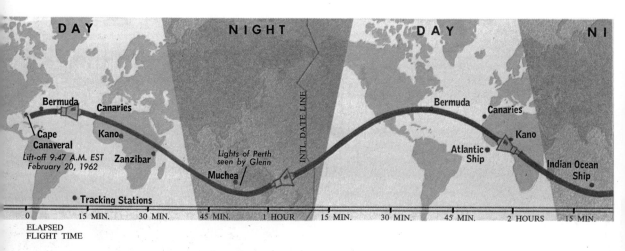

John H. Glenn orbits the earth three times for America. The track of spacecraft "Friendship 7" shows the crossing of three continents and three oceans in an undulating line representing an 81,000-mile space journey. Glenn moved through periods of alternating darkness and daylight. The areas of darkness are

place. A fireball re-entry resulted from this last minute decision which was made to ensure Glenn's safe return.

In his post-flight press conference held in the big tent at the Cape Canaveral test site, Glenn described how the chunks of flaming debris of the retro-rocket package had swept by his window during the 3000-degree Fahrenheit heat of re-entry. "There were moments of doubt whether the heat shield had been damaged," he said with a grin. "If that had happened, it might have been a bad day all around."

Glenn, like Shepard and Grissom before him, described the weightless state as a "very pleasant experience. I probably am becoming a Zero G addict." He gave the first human description of the beauty of a sunset in space in these poetic words: "As the sun goes down, it's very white, brilliant light, and as it goes down below the horizon you get a very bright orange color. Down close to the surface it pales out into a sort of blue, a darker blue, then off into black."

After describing the amazing phenomena of "luminous fireflies" that floated by his porthole window (later judged to be either frozen vapor crystals from his capsule's atmospheric exhaust or chips of paint), he related that one of the psychologists had inquired about the particles, asking: "What did they say, John?"

When President Kennedy flew down to Cape Canaveral to welcome Glenn home officially and decorate him with NASA's Distinguished Service Medal as America's first great space hero, he said, "We have a new ocean . . . and John Glenn is the admiral of that ocean." The crowd roared its approval when the President said: "Our boosters may not be as large as some others, but our men and women are."

Six days after the historic flight, Glenn stood before a joint session of Congress in the Nation's Capitol and said, "This has been a great experience for us all. I am glad to see that pride in our country and its accomplishments are not a thing of the past. I still get a hard-to-define feeling inside when the flag goes by and I know all of you do, too . . . Let us hope none of us ever loses that feeling."

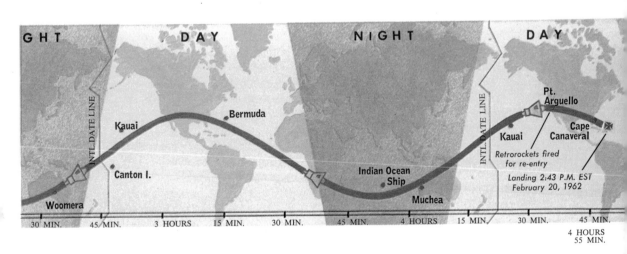

wider north of the equator due to the longer winter nights of the northern hemisphere. The total orbital time was 4 hours, 28 minutes; launch, re-entry and descent added another 27 minutes. A network of 16 tracking stations provided almost uninterrupted communications and telemetry data.

Christopher C. Kraft Jr.

Director of America's First Manned Space Flights

Little did Christopher Columbus Kraft's parents back in Phoebus, Virginia, realize that when they gave this name to their new son, born on February 28, 1924, he would one day be following in the exploratory paths of the famous Italian mariner who made the discovery of America possible. What they did not know then was that some 35 years later their son would not be sailing on well-charted oceans of water, but directing risky space flights of American men and monkeys into the uncharted cosmos.

Chris Kraft was also named after his father, who was born in New York at the time of the dedication at Columbus Circle of a monument to America's discoverer. Young Kraft was always blunt and outspoken, and not always tactful. Growing up in Hampton, Va., where many of aviation's advances were hatched, did not help to motivate young Kraft to become a pilot or space explorer. "All I ever hoped to do was play baseball," he said, speaking of his favorite sport in high school and college. "I didn't have any ambition to be director of anything." But after winning a baseball letter in college, he knew he would never become a professional because he was "too short." He then switched to engineering because he liked mathematics.

After graduating from the Virginia Polytechnic Institute with a degree in aeronautical engineering in 1944, Kraft joined the staff of the nearby Langley (Va.) Research Laboratory of the National Advisory Committee of Aeronautics. For 13 uneventful years, he worked hard at Langley, directing pilots in carrying out their flight tests. But nothing spectacular captured his attention in those days.

When NASA was formed around this older organization in 1958, Kraft was assigned as one of the original members of the Space Task Group, which was then in charge of Project Mercury. From that moment on, he became highly motivated by the challenges of space.

A born leader and manager, Kraft exerts authority as the Number One Flight Director in NASA's hierarchy. Kraft reports to Dr. Robert Gilruth, the Director of the Houston Manned Spacecraft Center, and former Director of Project Mercury. The relations between the two men are excellent.

Before moving to Texas, Kraft met Elizabeth Turnbull of nearby Hampton, Virginia, and married her. They later became the parents of a boy and a girl. He is the oldest of the four manned space flight directors assigned to the Houston Center.

Chris Kraft served as the NASA Flight Director for all of the original Mercury astronaut flights as well as the early Gemini flights. Following these early manned space successes, he was promoted to the post of Assistant Director for Flight Operations at the Houston Manned Spacecraft Center in November 1963, where he has been ever since. This perfectionist with a sense of humor has served his country well as the chief ground pilot for the astronauts who have carried our nation's flag into orbit with so much honor and glory.

With his ever-present cigar at his side, Kraft usually sits in his swivel chair behind the Mission Control console in his shirt-sleeves, as the general in charge of all phases of the flight operation from count-down-to-launch-to-recovery. Not until the astronauts are safely recovered by one of the waiting naval vessels in the recovery area does Chris Kraft relax, take off his headset — and light up his "victory" cigar to celebrate another successful American manned spaceflight operation.

Kraft usually has trouble sleeping the night before a launch, and will probably wake up around 2 A.M. which is about three hours before the astronauts are aroused at Cape Kennedy. Unlike the astronauts who immediately breakfast and suit-up, Kraft lies in bed stewing in his own juice, worrying about the flight, until he arises two hours later. At 4 A.M., the slightly built, dark-haired Kraft gets out of bed, has a quick breakfast and then drives his aged Chevy to the Mission Control Center which will become his home for the duration of each space flight — no matter how long its duration. (He shares a special bedroom with the other flight directors, located near the Mission Control Room.)

When Kraft arrives at his console, the countdown has already started back at Cape Kennedy. He may stop the count to check a problem or order it speeded up if necessary. When lift-off comes, he sees it only second-hand on the TV monitor, never live. Although he has yet to witness a live-launching of a manned spaceship, he gets just as much of a thrill at viewing the remote lift-off as do those onlookers who are at the press site watching the ascent from Cape Kennedy.

Kraft views the six-minute initial powered phase of each space flight as the "toughest part of the flight" — since they are never routine. It is during this critical period that so much can go wrong causing a mission abort and necessitating the quick firing of the escape system to free the space crew from the launch vehicle. Although this drastic action never had to be taken during the entire Mercury program or the Gemini missions, Kraft knows that one day the responsibility will fall on his shoulders or those of one of his assistant mission directors to bring back the astronauts before they ever get into orbit.

The anticipation of such a dire event during the critical moments of lift-off served as a partial explanation for the rise in Kraft's pulse to 136 beats per minute which was usually higher than that of most astronauts in their capsule. When-and-if Kraft ever threw an "Abort" switch on his console, a red light would immediately flash on the spacecraft instrument panel, directing the astronauts inside to fire the emergency escape rocket system.

Mercury Control Center at Cape Canaveral. It is now called Cape Kennedy.

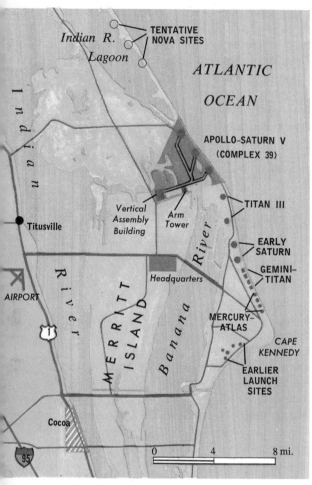

John F. Kennedy Space Center, launch site for U.S. manned space flights.

MAP LABELS:
Indian R. Lagoon

TENTATIVE NOVA SITES

ATLANTIC OCEAN

APOLLO–SATURN V (COMPLEX 39)

Indian River

Titusville

Vertical Assembly Building

Arm Tower

TITAN III

River

EARLY SATURN

GEMINI–TITAN

Headquarters

AIRPORT

River

MERRITT ISLAND

Banana River

MERCURY–ATLAS

CAPE KENNEDY

EARLIER LAUNCH SITES

Cocoa

0   4   8 mi.

During each flight, he exercises the full direction of controlling the entire operation, assimilating a continuous flow of information that is received at Mission Control from a team of experts located at key tracking stations around the world. When not directing the progress of a particular space flight (for which he has recently delegated the responsibility to one of three assistants who each take eight-hour turns at the console during long missions), Kraft continues to exercise management responsibilities in three divisions of the Manned Spacecraft Center in Houston.

In the performance of his many duties, Kraft supervises the close teamwork between the various flight controllers, who are monitoring different parts of the mission. Never trusting to computers completely, Kraft and his team stand between the astronauts and their gadget-filled spacecraft, watching every moment to make sure that all is well aboard. The astronauts know that the flight director on the ground controls their mission and they have faith in his decisions, whether they be a "go" for another orbit or a command to re-enter the atmosphere for an abrupt end.

Occasionally, however, the astronauts in space will suggest an alternate course of action through their CapCom (Capsule Communicator, another astronaut sitting at a console in front of Kraft), and the Flight Director will usually concur if it does not radically alter the purpose of the mission or safety of the crew.

Kraft's most important spaceflight directorial decision, however, did not concern the fate of a human astronaut in orbit, but that of a primate, Enos. The astrochimp had been placed in orbit on November 29, 1961, in a planned three-orbit test of the Mercury capsule just before John Glenn was to make his historic flight early the following year. Midway through the second trip around the earth, the capsule suddenly started to oscillate violently, buffeting the chimpanzee passenger inside. Kraft had less than 20 seconds to decide whether to bring the spacecraft down as the capsule came within view of the California tracking station at Point Arguello.

Kraft turned to a spacecraft engineer for advice on what to do with the wobbling spacecraft that seemed to have a jammed altitude control thruster. After conferring with his assistant briefly, he decided to bring the capsule down prematurely. Flashing word to California to bring it down, Kraft conducted his own countdown for the re-entry. The capsule containing Enos splashed down safely off Bermuda and was recovered just over an hour later in excellent condition. His quick response in this ticklish situation probably saved the life of the chimp and kept our manned space program on schedule, preventing further delays that had already caused us to lose the first manned space heat to the Soviets and their new hero Yuri Gagarin.

Between flights, Kraft conducts exhaustive simulated astronaut training flights with his assistants, sandwiched in among his visits to various other NASA and industry installations around the country. When he is satisfied with the progress made in all the preparatory steps for a particular upcoming flight, he then sets the launch date. On the day of the flight, if the weather report is positive, Kraft is at his happiest. "That's what we live for," he remarks. Kraft even has been able to get over an ulcer that he acquired while working at Langley, although most men would probably get several ulcers from such a nerve-wracking task as is now his.

Kraft is almost fatalistic about the possibility of astronauts being killed in orbit. "Inevitably, some of these guys are going to meet with an accident of some sort," he said. "They themselves can make a mistake as can we on the ground, or something may go wrong with the spacecraft. All we can do is make sure that most of these things aren't fatal."

The irony of the United States space efforts to date is that six astronauts have lost their lives in aircraft or ground accidents. A flash fire during a general static test of Apollo 1 on January 27, 1967 resulted in the deaths of Virgil Grissom, Edward White, and Roger Chaffee. Three other astronauts died in airplane crashes in the line of duty.

With the completion of the Gemini flights — including one for 14 days — this country accumulated almost 1,900 man hours of space flight with no deaths or injuries in orbit and only one close call, the aborted flight of *Gemini 8* on March 16, 1966. After the first space docking was achieved with an Agena spacecraft on that date, a maneuvering propulsion unit malfunctioned and the

flight was ended abruptly 16 hours and 42 minutes into the mission.

Kraft has dreamed that he would like to go into orbit himself some day — "if they could put one up and bring one down without the rigors of acceleration and deceleration. I think it would be fabulous to view the earth, the stars, and the moon from up there. The dream of all of us is to develop the capability to reach the planets. The moon is merely a stepping stone."

For Kraft's role as director of the six highly successful Mercury space flights, President John F. Kennedy presented him with the NASA Distinguished Service Medal on May 21, 1963. The citation was, "For his outstanding leadership in the planning and operational control of the space flight mission of the United States in Project Mercury." While Kraft was chief of the former Flight Operations Division of Manned Spacecraft Center, the division was presented a Group Achievement Award by NASA Administrator James E. Webb on October 25, 1962.

For Kraft, who has received many other outstanding awards since, these citations represent part of the satisfaction he has obtained over the years for performing his key task of helping to guide our astronauts safely into space — and back.

Kraft at flight directions console at Houston Manned Spacecraft Center.

William H. Pickering

Builder of America's First Earth Satellite

In November 1957, following the launching of the first two Soviet Sputniks, a troubled White House gave the Jet Propulsion Laboratory and the Army Ballistic Missile Agency the dual assignment of regaining our tarnished national prestige in space. The much ballyhooed Vanguard had failed to get off the launch pad after several frustrating attempts, yet within 83 days, the ABMA team headed by Dr. Wernher von Braun and the JPL team under Dr. William Hayward Pickering successfully orbited America's first earth satellite on January 31, 1958.

That night a happy Pickering, von Braun, who provided the Jupiter–C booster rocket, and Dr. James Van Allen of Iowa State University, who provided the instrumentation that went inside the satellite, were accorded a tumultuous reception in the great hall of the National Academy of Sciences in Washington. Although the 18-pound Explorer 1 weighed only one-tenth that of the first Sputnik, it did help us to recover from the serious blow to our national pride as well as to make the most important discovery of the International Geophysical Year — the finding of the Van Allen radiation belt around the earth.

The news photographs published at the time of the three smiling American space scientists holding aloft a replica of the long, cylindrical-shaped artificial earth satellite over their heads, warmed the hearts of most of our citizenry who had waited for many frustrating months for this happy moment.

William Pickering was born in Wellington, New Zealand, on December 24, 1910, the son of a pharmacist. In 1920, when Bill was 10 years old, he read a brief article about a new wireless method of sending and receiving messages, called radio. The article concerned the "transmission of electromagnetic waves with assigned frequencies." In a local high school, he joined a Radio Club composed of ham radio operators. Pickering and his fellow students built a ham radio station and mastered the intricacies of the Morse Code. Although he found little further scientific information about this new invention in the local library, unconsciously, Bill had started himself on a career that began to blossom in earnest after his graduation from Wellington High School in 1927.

The next step in his education saw him enrolling as a freshman in Canterbury College, the engineering school of the University of New Zealand, located in Christchurch. But during his first summer's vacation, he faced a crucial decision. A visiting uncle, Horace Duslin, a mining engineer, who maintained a home in Los Angeles, persuaded young Pickering to leave New Zealand and come to America so that he could enroll at the prestigious California Institute of Technology in Pasadena.

In March 1929, he made his decision and embarked on an ocean liner for the New World. Because Pickering came from New Zealand, the authorities at Cal Tech were not sure that his educational background would measure up to their stiff requirements. So Pickering was not permitted a student visa but had to come in as an immigrant. After taking the University's quarterly examination, however, he showed strong evidence of his fine training and potential and was soon welcomed to Cal Tech as a full-fledged student.

Pickering received his B.S. degree in 1932, M.S. in 1933 and his Ph.D. in Physics, cum laude, in 1936. While working on the latter degrees, he came into contact with the Nobel Laureate, Dr. Robert Millikan, who was President of the institution, and a lasting friendship was soon formed. Millikan gave him a faculty appointment as an instructor in electrical engineering. This marked the beginning of a rise up to a full professorship by 1946.

Meanwhile, he became deeply involved with Dr. Millikan in an official "moonlighting" sideline to his teaching — cosmic ray research. "My first work with Millikan in this area," he reminisced, "was building Geiger counters and using them as tools for investigating cosmic rays. About 1930, Geiger wrote his first work on the counters which are now the accepted instruments for measuring the ionizing particles in the air. We began flying Geiger counters as high as the balloons would go — about 100,000 feet. The essential problem was to take the instruments up to that altitude and send the cosmic ray information back by radio where it was recorded on the ground. We were primarily interested in a worldwide survey of the variations in cosmic ray intensity at high altitudes, and so we went on a number of expeditions to Mexico, India, and other places. It was fascinating to travel with Millikan to various parts of the world; he was interested not only in all phases of science, but in all phases of life."

When World War II broke out, Pickering returned from one of these expeditions to JPL at Cal Tech where he served throughout the duration of that conflict. During the war JPL operated behind a high wall of secrecy in its canyon location just north of Pasadena. It achieved some remarkable firsts in rocketry after Pearl Harbor, including the first JATO jet-assisted-takeoff under the guidance of Dr. Theodore von Kármán and his Suicide Club. Local irate citizens sought to disband the organization during these hectic war years, not because of the noise that was generated from its test stands, but because of "the hearses that left JPL every night sneaking out the day's casualties." Patiently, Pickering and the lab people had to explain to the citizenry, that

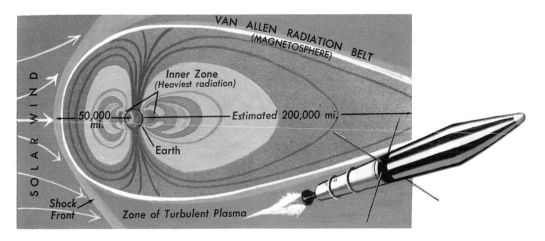

Explorer 1, America's first satellite relayed the startling news that the globe is enveloped by a layer of hazardous radiation trapped in the earth's magnetic field.

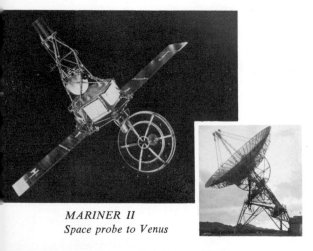

MARINER II
Space probe to Venus

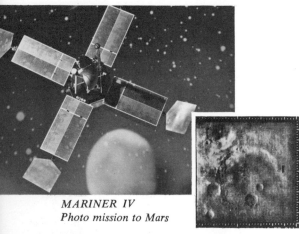

MARINER IV
Photo mission to Mars

SURVEYOR 1
Soft landing on the Moon

Some of the milestones of U.S. space exploration — all achievements of Jet Propulsion Laboratory and Dr. Pickering.

the "hearses" were really convoys bearing missiles from the JPL location to faraway proving grounds, with police escort, under cover of darkness.

In 1950, already associated with the Jet Propulsion Laboratory for six years, he was made responsible for the development of the U.S. Army Corporal missile, America's first long-range liquid-propelled supersonic missile capable of tactical application. This project reached culmination in 1954 when Corporal battalions, completely equipped and trained, were sent to overseas stations. Following Corporal, the Sergeant solid-propellant missile was developed at JPL under the direction of Dr. Pickering.

Dr. Pickering was appointed JPL Director in 1954 at a time when the mission of the Laboratory was to originate, develop, and test new guided missile systems; to conduct supporting research investigations in physical sciences for the purpose of acquiring basic data applicable to the varied aspects of weapon-system development; and to undertake feasibility and evaluation studies of proposed and/or previously initiated programs of special interest to the nation as a whole.

With the transfer of JPL to the National Aeronautics and Space Administration in December 1958, the talents of the Laboratory were reoriented toward space vehicles and missions. Currently, JPL is responsible for research and development programs in the unmanned exploration of the moon, the planets, and interplanetary space.

Under Dr. Pickering's direction, the Mariner 2 spacecraft successfully completed a fly-by of the planet Venus on December 14, 1962, culminating a 109-day journey of over 180.2 million miles. This date marks the birth of the interplanetary age, indicating the first time that man had penetrated the depths of space to the vicinity of another planet and obtained first-hand information.

The moon, too, came under the close scrutiny of JPL scientists on July 31, 1964. The successful flight of Ranger 7 radioed to earth 4,316 high resolution pictures of the lunar surface which proved to be 2,000 times better than those produced by the best earth-based telescopes. For this unprecedented accomplishment, Dr. Pickering received the personal congratulations of President Lyndon B. Johnson.

On July 14, 1965, a Mariner spacecraft, sailing under JPL colors, passed within 7,000 miles of the planet Mars. Its television camera scanned the surface of the red planet and relayed 22 photographs back to earth some 10 hours later. The historic first closeups of Mars showed a heavily cratered surface but left open the question of possible life on the barren planet.

The most recent success was the spectacular Surveyor I soft landing on the moon in June 1966, which took over 1,000 close-up pictures of the lunar surface near the crater Flamsteed. This JPL spacecraft was successful on the first try. It compared favorably with the Soviet Luna 9 which had followed five failures before it made a soft landing on the moon.

Pickering has received many honors since becoming head of JPL. He has been elected President of the International Astronautical Federation, the first President of the Institute of Aeronautics and Astronautics, and he has been awarded the Distinguished Civilian Service Award by the President of the United States, as well as the Columbus Gold Medal and the James Wyld Memorial Award of the American Rocket Society, among other awards.

Pickering is one of the few space scientists who has been willing to speculate openly about the future, not only in his own professional field, but of the world around us. With technology making possible a greater amount of leisure time available to us in the future, Pickering asks a thoughtful and penetrating question:

"Is man able to rise to the opportunity which is presented to him; does he have the spiritual and emotional resources to live the good life that physical science makes possible, or will he allow his technological capability to be a Frankenstein monster and conquer him either physically or spiritually? ...The problem which mankind must solve, if we are to continue to maintain any sort of civilized life on this planet, is no longer the physical one of struggling to provide food and shelter for the family, but a spiritual one of learning to live with the rest of the human species, in a world filled with the products of modern technology."

As one of our first space leaders who called for a stepped-up national space program, beginning in 1959 long before the second Soviet cosmic shocks were wrought by the manned space flights of Gagarin and Titov in 1961, Pickering ranks as one of the few Americans on the inside who had the courage to speak out about the slow pace of our space programs. That he survived these criticisms of the policy of his superiors has marked the character of the man and his work.

Pickering has also advocated what many believe to be a startling concept: "It must surely be obvious to all of us," he says, "that science is playing an increasingly important role, both in our everyday life and in the national and international activities of the nations of the world. Surely it follows that in the future it will be essential for the educated man to be literate in science, just as in the past the educated man had to be literate in the classics. This will be so because science will play a vital role in every activity of daily life . . . (People) must be led out of their science-fiction and pseudo-science dreams into the world of scientific reality."

Pickering is a man who is helping to lead up to that reality as the Space Age continues to unfold. He made a decision early in life to lead himself and the new radio device out of its infancy by finding ways to adapt it to help unravel the mysteries of space. It seems fair to assume that he will go on providing leadership in this area for many years to come.

Edward H. White II

First American Astronaut to Walk in Space

During the 1,600,000-mile flight of *Gemini 4* in early June 1965, one of the two astronauts aboard, Major Edward White II, successfully carried out the first extravehicular (EVA) activity of the United States' manned spaceflight program. It was on June 3rd, during the third revolution, that Major White opened the hatch and prepared to take his walk in space.

The capsule was orbiting at an altitude of 120 miles over the Pacific Ocean, when White left his spacecraft with Command Pilot Major James McDivitt, USAF, remaining at the controls of the tiny vehicle traveling at 17,500 miles an hour. White clung to a thin lifeline as he moved about outside *Gemini 4,* even taking a picture of the spacecraft from the outside, the first time that this feat had ever been accomplished. (The Russians had sent one of their cosmonauts, Major Alexei Leonov, for a short, 10-minute space walk a few months earlier, but the pictures sent back of his cosmic feat were quite fuzzy.)

Prior to White's space walk, an effort had been made to rendezvous the *Gemini 4* with an orbiting second-stage of the Titan II launch vehicle. But since the booster was in such a different orbit from that of the spacecraft and was tumbling end-over-end, too much fuel was expended in the maneuver so the experiment had to be abandoned; otherwise there would not have been enough fuel left both for the space walk and re-entry.

The purpose of space walking was not an acrobatic, dramatic stunt. Rather it signified an important advance in the techniques of transferring from one space vehicle to another, monitoring the docking of two vehicles in orbit, and making adjustments outside of a spacecraft. EVA would also be an essential step needed to help achieve a successful Apollo man-on-the-moon effort, which would include the transfer of two of

the three lunarnauts from the mothership to the Lunar Excursion Module, before its descent to the moon's surface.

White and McDivitt had been practicing for this moment together for nearly a year since they had been named as the flight crew for the *Gemini 4* mission. They had rehearsed the countdown, launch, orbital flight, space walk, re-entry and recovery dozens of times in ground simulators before they made their actual flight.

On the historic June 3, 1965, there had been one long moment of suspense during the final portions of the countdown, when the Titan's launch erector tower failed to lower properly. Before this adjustment was successfully made, an hour and 16 minutes had elapsed which delayed their launch from the programmed 10 A.M. to 11:16 A.M. But from that moment on, the launch and insertion into orbit followed a textbook pattern as the astronauts prepared for the adventures to come in orbit.

The live radio transcript of the actual space walk made it possible for millions of people around the world to listen to this dramatic event. Although several days elapsed before the spectacular color film was released after the astronauts' return from space, the running, verbal account of the highlights of their mission with the various capsule communicators located at ground tracking stations around the earth accented the listeners' suspense. Excerpts of the official "Mission Commentary," picking up the flight in the third revolution, read as follows:

GEMINI CONTROL (Paul Haney, NASA public affairs officer): "Four hours and 24 minutes into the mission. The Hawaii station has just established contact with the pilot, Jim McDivitt, who advises that the cabin has been depressurized. We are standing by for a GO from Hawaii to open the hatch. . . . White has opened the door. He has stood up. . . ."

FLIGHT DIRECTOR, Houston: "Tell him we're ready to have him get out when he is ready."

GEMINI: "He's ready to egress (exit) right now." (At this suspenseful point, communication with *Gemini 4* was lost for a few moments as the spacecraft passed out of range of the Hawaii station, until a waiting world picked them up again through the facilities of the NASA-Guaymas, Mexico, station.)

GEMINI CONTROL: " 'Gus' Grissom (the capsule communicator in Houston) has just established contact with the spacecraft. McDivitt confirmed that White did leave the spacecraft. He said he looks great. . . ."

WHITE: "The maneuvering unit is good. The only problem I have is that I haven't got enough fuel. I've exhausted the fuel now and I was able to maneuver myself down to the bottom of the spacecraft. I'm looking right down, and it looks like we are coming up on the coast of California, and I'm doing a slow rotation to the right. There is absolutely no disorientation association."

McDIVITT: "One thing about it, when Ed gets out there and starts whipping around it sure makes the spacecraft tough to control. . . ."

WHITE: "I'm going to work on getting some pictures, Jim."

McDIVITT: "O.K. Get out in front where I can see you again. . . . Where are you?"

WHITE: "Right out in front now. I don't have the control I had any more. . . . There's no difficulty in recontacting the spacecraft . . . particularly in trying to move back. . . . I'm very thankful in having the experience to be first."

McDIVITT: "Ed, will you please roll around? Right now we're pointing just about straight down to the ground."

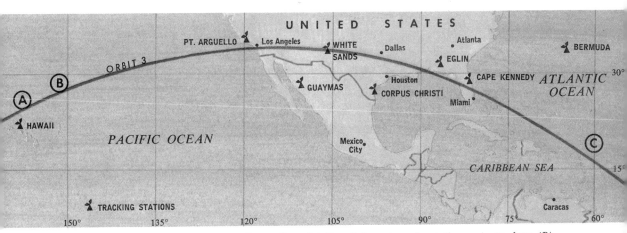

Maj. White opened the hatch of Gemini 4 near Hawaii (A) and then stepped out three minutes later (B) remaining outside the capsule until south of Bermuda (C) making his walk in space 6000 miles long.

59

WHITE: "O.K., now I'm taking a look back at the adapter. . . . The thrusters are clean. The sun in space is not blinding, but it's quite nice. I'm coming back down on the spacecraft. I can sit out here and see the whole California coast." (He said this while looking through the dark sunvisor which he had lowered over his helmet to keep from being blinded by the bright sun.)

FLIGHT SURGEON: "Flight, this is Surgeon. The data looks great here."

FLIGHT DIRECTOR: "How's his EKG (electrocardiogram)?"

FLIGHT SURGEON: "It looks great, Flight. He's just ripping along here at a great rate."

McDIVITT: "You smeared up my windshield, you dirty dog! You see how it's all smeared up there?" (There was much laughter at the Manned Spacecraft Center in Houston at the command pilot's remark to White. Radio listeners, too, were amused at this typical American bit of humor.)

WHITE: (answering nonchalantly) "Yep!"

McDIVITT: "Looks like there's a coating on the outside and you've rubbed it off. That's apparently what you've done."

Before reluctantly coming back inside the spacecraft, White spent a total of 21 minutes outside the capsule. This was twice as long as the Russian walk made four months earlier. The control of his movements using the Hand-Held Self Maneuvering Unit (a Buck Rogers space gun) gave him perfect control of his extravehicular movements. After his rocket gun was exhausted, he discovered that he could still maneuver about, using the tether as a guide.

As White re-entered the spacecraft, this conversation took place:

WHITE: "O.K., I'm on top of it now."

McDIVITT: "O.K., you're right on top. Come on in then. . . ."

WHITE: "All right."

McDIVITT: "I'll put the gun up."

WHITE: "I'll open the door and come through there."

McDIVITT: "O.K. Let's not lose this camera now. I don't quite have it. A little bit more. O.K., I've got it. . . . Come on. Let's get back in here before it gets dark."

But there was one final complication. After returning to the inside of the capsule, White discovered that the hatch door failed to close and lock normally. So the fastening had to be maneuvered into place and secured painstakingly. As a consequence, the *Gemini 4* was never depressurized afterward, as originally planned, in order to dispose of excess materials no longer needed. Therefore, this excess equipment had to be carried throughout the remainder of the flight which cluttered their capsule.

Despite this inconvenience, they had proved that man could leave his spacecraft in orbit and maneuver in space successfully without any physical harm or strain. Furthermore, *Gemini 4* marked only the second manned-orbital flight of that new space series. Their 62 orbits completed before splashdown signified a big jump over the previous three-orbit flight of *Gemini 3* piloted by Astronauts Virgil Grissom and John Young. The total space flying time of White and McDivitt covered 97 hours and 56 minutes, and ranked their endeavor as one of the longest and most successful flights in our space program to date. The bearded and tired White and McDivitt were ultimately picked up by a helicopter after their splashdown in the Atlantic on June 7th, and flown to the carrier *Wasp*.

White was a graduate of both West Point, and the University of Michigan where he received a Master of Science degree in aeronautical engineering. The Air Force Major, who was born in Texas, was 34 years old when he made his historic space walk. He had to wait almost three years to get a chance to go into orbit after being selected as a member of NASA's second group of astronauts in September 1962. Prior to entering the space program, White compiled more than 3,600 hours of flying time, many of them in jets.

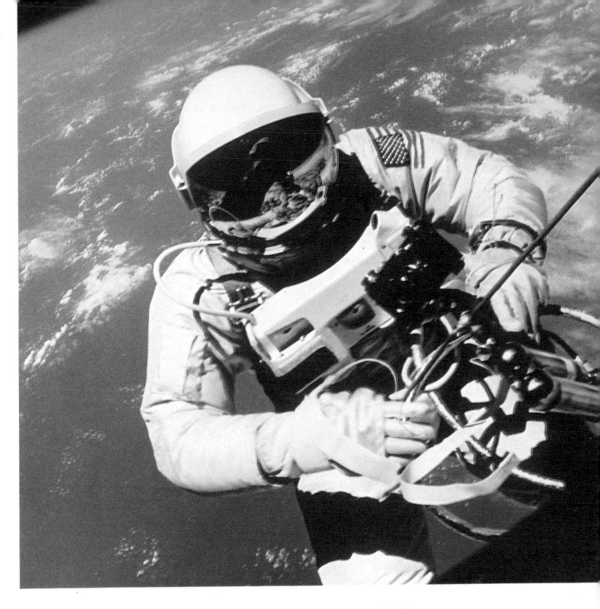

Secured to spacecraft by a golden umbilical line, Maj. White maneuvers freely in space.

On October 8, 1965, four months after his historic extravehicular activity, White and McDivitt presented U.N. Secretary General U Thant with the blue United Nations flag that White carried inside his spacesuit during his space walk. In presenting the flag to the U.N. executive, White pointed out that this was the same flag that his father, an Air Force Colonel, had carried in Korea in 1950 when he was a commander of an air transport wing attached to the U.N. forces during that conflict.

The astronaut said that from the great distances of outer space the boundaries of individual countries are not visible. "The people of the world are bound together in the space age," he asserted. In reply, U Thant expressed his thought that the astronaut's "view of the world from outer space is the only correct one."

People everywhere felt a great loss on January 27, 1967 when they learned that Edward White and two fellow astronauts, Virgil Grissom and Roger Chaffee, died in a flash fire in their *Apollo 1* capsule during a static test on a launch pad at Cape Kennedy. White was buried with full military honors at West Point.

Robert J. Parks

Director of Our First Instrument Landing on the Moon

When Surveyor I made its historic first American soft-landing on the moon and started to transmit back its many thousands of clear pictures of the lunar surface in early June 1966, President Johnson complimented the members of the NASA and industry crew that built this spacecraft for adding "another exciting chapter in the peaceful exploration of the universe. Overnight," the President concluded, "the eyes of Surveyor I have become the eyes of the world on the moon."

To Robert J. Parks, the Surveyor Program Manager for NASA's Jet Propulsion Laboratory (a branch of the California Institute of Technology), this was the moment that he had waited for during its six hectic years of development.

Parks, aged 44, the chief of the Surveyor spacecraft program, is known as a "cool cookie" among his colleagues at the Jet Propulsion Laboratory. He has been deeply enmeshed in rocketry and space projects for over 20 years, starting with the development of the first Corporal guided missile built by JPL in the the late nineteen-forties. He gradually progressed his way up the administrative ladder to head more complex space programs until he was given the responsibility for the risky Surveyor with its 100,000 component parts.

"The pressure of the space program has ground up a lot of good men," one official at the laboratory said. "Bob Parks has aged 15 years in the last five, but he's the kind of tough resilient guy who can carry an enormous load."

Parks, who was responsible for the overall construction of the Surveyor and guiding its difficult mission to the moon, had to weather storms of criticism as the project met unavoidable delays and cost overruns. (The program had run three years behind schedule and had cost $800 million — more than 10 times the original estimate.) Despite the cries of mismanagement, Parks brought his project to an astoundingly successful conclusion on the first try as compared with the Soviets who tried five times before their less sophisticated Luna 9 made it to the moon.

But, as one happy NASA official put it: "We had thought it would take three or four flights to get our spacecraft operational." The success of Surveyor I not only saved us money, but speeded up the day when we could send men to the moon, since it proved that the basic design of the LEM (lunar excursion module of the manned Apollo program) was sound.

Parks was born in Los Angeles on April 1, 1922. He grew up in Southern California, attending the Newport Harbor Union High School. After graduation he enrolled in the California Institute of Technology and four years later received a Bachelor of Science degree in Electrical Engineering. He then served two and a half years in the Army Signal Corps, spending eight months with our occupation forces in Europe at the conclusion of World War II.

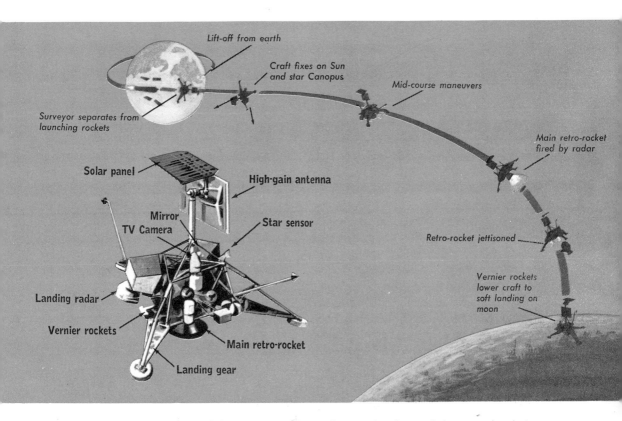

Lift-off from earth

Craft fixes on Sun and star Canopus

Mid-course maneuvers

Surveyor separates from launching rockets

Main retro-rocket fired by radar

Solar panel

High-gain antenna

Mirror
TV Camera

Star sensor

Retro-rocket jettisoned

Vernier rockets lower craft to soft landing on moon

Landing radar

Vernier rockets

Main retro-rocket

Landing gear

After Surveyor 1 was hurled toward the moon its solar panels were aimed toward the sun and a navigation sensor was fixed on the star Canopus. During the long coast to the target a series of course maneuvers reoriented the craft for the final approach. The main retro rockets fired 52 miles above the moon.

In Vienna, he met a vivacious Austrian girl, Johanna Richter, who was serving as a translator. They were married shortly thereafter. Returning to the United States, Parks worked briefly with Hughes Aircraft Co. as a radio engineer, but after the urging of several friends, he joined the Jet Propulsion Laboratory in April 1957, where he has been ever since.

Before being designated the head of the Surveyor program by Dr. Pickering, Parks served as assistant director of the lunar and planetary projects at the laboratory, whose mission is to explore the surface of the moon, Mars, and Venus. In 1962, he supervised the successful shot of the Mariner 2 spacecraft that passed within 20,000 miles of Venus.

One associate recalls that during the first Corporal missile flight, which zoomed up for only 100 miles, the tension was so great that after its successful completion, Parks and his assistants simply "sat down right there in the New Mexican desert and looked dazed for a few minutes."

Recalling that incident almost 20 years later, Parks noted: "If someone had told me at the time that we would be landing a craft on the moon by 1966, I would have told him he was crazy. I never thought we could have come this far this fast."

Several times during the hectic Surveyor I flight, Parks, taut, intense, and puffing nervously on the stub of a cigar, delivered terse but articulate briefings on the progress of the mission to the 150 assembled reporters and government officials. This included the successful mid-course maneuver to change the flightpath and help insure a successful landing. The spacecraft was told to roll almost 90 degrees, then yaw off its path almost 60 degrees and finally perform a second roll of 94 degrees in order to point its large retro-rocket motor in the proper direction to reduce its approach velocity.

Although one of the two TV transmitting antennae on the side of the spacecraft failed to unfold properly in flight, it did not appear that the ability of its roving camera eye to take pictures and relay them back to earth after landing would be impeded. Even the most critical part of the journey, the slowing down of the spacecraft during the terminal maneuver, went off without a flaw.

At 11:17 P.M. (PDT) on June 1, 1966, the 620-pound U.S. Surveyor I spacecraft soft-landed on the moon just south of the lunar equator. After speeding to our lunar satellite at over 5,800 m.p.h., it virtually halted in space, then touched down at less than 8 m.p.h. after being further slowed by small vernier rockets.

It arrived just five seconds late after a journey of 63 hours and 247,529 miles. And it landed almost precisely on target, just north of the crater Flamsteed in the Ocean of Storms. The slight jolt of landing corrected whatever was wrong with one of the two antennae and it snapped into place. Within minutes, it began sending hundreds of brilliant pictures of the lunar surface back to earth. And suddenly to millions of people on the earth, particularly television viewers, the moon was closer than their own backyards.

After Surveyor I had sent back its 10,388 televised pictures in less than two weeks, Parks and other NASA officials held a press conference and concluded that: "The moon is a very gritty, bouldery, pebbly, silt-like place, apparently a sort of neutral gray." They also concluded that astronauts walking there would not be in "much danger of falling into a hole." The fact that the three-legged Surveyor did not sink into the lunar surface, but instead rested comfortably on firm lunar terrain, augured well for the Apollo program.

In the 12 days and nine hours of responding to over 100,000 earth-to-moon radio commands before the long lunar night set in, Surveyor sent back the most remarkable and clear set of close-up pictures of the moon's surface in the flat plain where it landed, far surpassing the few fuzzier pictures sent back by the Soviet Luna 9 earlier in the year.

Surveyor even managed to send back a bonus set of pictures 19 minutes after the lunar sunset, when it sent back some remarkable photos of the lunar landscape faintly illuminated by earthshine.

The Surveyor stood alone in the deep freeze of the 14-day lunar night as a solitary artifact of men who lived on another body in the solar system some 240,000 miles distant. For Robert Parks and his team at the Jet Propulsion Laboratory, it marked the successful conclusion of a long, uphill battle to justify the prolonged and expensive agony that their project entailed.

Although Surveyor did not settle the mystery of the origin of the moon, the nature of its "seas" (marias), or the source

The surface of the moon as seen by Surveyor 1. This mosaic was made from several hundred photographs taken by the spacecraft.

of the glassy, streamlined chips strewn over much of the earth, it did bring the eventual solutions to these and other allied questions within our grasp for the first time.

After sleeping through a two-week lunar night, where the temperature reached 280 degrees below zero F., Surveyor was surprisingly revived after being subjected to a week of warming in the sun during a new lunar day. It took 319 more pictures after its battery temperature had temporarily risen ominously to 140 degrees F., signaling that the remarkable unmanned U.S. spacecraft was at last dying of a lunar fever. Even in its death throes, Surveyor I continued to confound its builders with its tenacious ability to cling to life beyond its normal life expectancy. Its "remarkable" and "unpredictable" extended life, which included a clear picture of a cracked mirror covering of a thermal radiator on its battery box, helped to salve the criticisms that marked Surveyor's long and expensive gestation period.

Parks worked around-the-clock on the Surveyor program as its launch time neared.

In more normal times, his job required 60 to 70 hours a week. For relaxation, he, his wife, and their three teen-aged sons enjoy skiing on the slopes at Aspen, Colorado, or water skiing in the blue Pacific.

"Tough physical sports take his mind off his work," said Mrs. Parks. "Bob also has worked hard in recent years to get his pilot's license." He finally received it a few months before Surveyor was sent to the moon. He loves to take his family on short airplane hops around the state when he can spare the time.

His wife concedes that the demands of the space program are often the source of family grumbling. "We'd like to see more of him, but the work takes so much of his time. Any wife in my position would do a great deal of worrying about her husband's health." She tries to get him to relax when he drives up to their mountaintop home overlooking the San Gabriel Valley and the JPL complex. This retreat, which has a superb view of the ocean and sky, is a fitting place to live and think — for a man preoccupied with space.

Close-up of the Surveyor landing foot resting on lunar surface indicates a loose, gritty layer that should easily support men.

Pillow-sized rock and a small impact crater show in photo taken a few hours after Surveyor 1 landed.

John W. Young — Michael Collins

The Nearly Flawless Space Flight of Gemini 10

For three days in July 1966, from the 18th to the 21st, a Navy Commander and an Air Force Major piloted the most successful space flight made to date by any nation. John Young and Michael Collins, with the help of their *Gemini 10* capsule and the reliable Titan and Agena rockets, were able to perform a whole series of difficult missions in space that brought the encomium "flawless" from Dr. Robert Gilruth, the Director of the Manned Spacecraft Center, as he described their flight in a post-mission summation.

Almost everything went according to plan, from the near perfect double countdown of the Agena/Atlas and the Gemini Titan rockets to the many "firsts" which they achieved during their historic 70-hour, 46-minute mission. In the pages of their space log the Gemini astronauts were able to record the fact that they flew deeper into space (475 miles) than man, including the Soviets, had yet penetrated; had spent the most time (nearly 39 hours) linked with an Agena satellite after a tricky rendezvous and docking space maneuver; had fired the rocket engine of the captured satellite, and had reached yet another satellite, Agena 8, placed there months earlier, thus making the first dual rendevous in space.

In addition, Major Collins became the first man to make physical contact with another orbiting object and actually retrieved a scientific instrument package that had been placed in space.

During this "smoothest flight yet" in which the twin astronauts discovered that the earth "really was round" they established a record for negative reporting — the lack of comment by them to the ground. The two taciturn men kept so quiet for such long periods that they began to worry the ground controllers. About 24 hours into the mission Flight Crew Operations Director, Donald "Deke" Slayton, one of the original seven Mercury astronauts, went on the communications link to tell them "... You guys are doing a commendable job of maintaining radio silence. Since the French stopped shooting at you, why don't you do a little more talking from now on." (Slayton was referring to the French airdrop nuclear test that took place in the Pacific during their mission. But the mushroom cloud and atomic flash occurred while the astronauts were over the Atlantic, so they were in little danger of being blinded by the glare.)

Five hours after their launching, the two astronauts made a successful rendezvous with the Agena 10 after a 103,000-mile chase and then docked with this unmanned spacecraft an hour later, only to discover that they had used up twice as much fuel to achieve this part of the mission than planned. Collins described their link-up with the Agena 10 as being "like a railroad engineer driving down the road with a big freight train. All you can see is the freight train." (The Gemini's nose in the docked position was facing away from their line of flight, looking backward toward the Agena.)

With the Agena's 16,000-pound engine now their source of propulsion, the tandem vehicle was ready for a new orbit. Young fired Agena's engine to hurl the astronauts into a higher egg-shaped orbit with an apogee of 475 miles. The spacecraft's high orbit took them through the South Atlantic Anomaly, the area where the Van Allen radiation belt dips unusually close to the earth. The radiation levels were much less than NASA scientists had expected and well within safe limits.

After several hours of sleep and a Spartan Gemini breakfast of toast and bacon strips, Young and Collins prepared for their next task, rendezvous with the Agena 8. The target had been left in orbit four months previously during the ill-fated mission of *Gemini 8*. Young fired the Agena's large thruster once more, this time as a braking action to place them just inside the circular path of Agena 8, now some 1200 miles ahead. While they waited to catch up, Collins opened the right side hatch and stood up, with his head and shoulders in space, in order to take pictures of the stars with ultra-violet sensitive film.

As Collins moved about in his tight-fitting hatch until he felt at home in the darkness of space, Young noticed an extremely bright object out of his porthole. He said it was too bright to be a planet and suggested that it could be the Agena 8 but ground controllers quickly calculated that the Agena 8 was still about 1073 nautical miles from their craft.

Soon thereafter both Young and Collins experienced serious discomfort from swollen and watering eyes, caused by water vapor penetrating into their lithium hydroxide canister that was used to cleanse their cabin air of carbon dioxide. Young abruptly ordered termination of the standup EVA (extra vehicular activity) but failed to report it to earth. "I figured I'd just be a sissy," he said later. "My eyes were watering . . . and when it gets so bad you can't see what you're doing, it's time to call it off." He called to Collins to close the hatch and get back into his seat quickly, which he did. A few minutes later, the air in the cabin cleared and they could see normally again. They had experienced a similar eye irritation to that undergone by the *Gemini 4* crew in June of the previous year.

The "bright object" seen on the second day was not the only sighting of an unknown object from space. Astronauts Edward White and James McDivitt had ob-

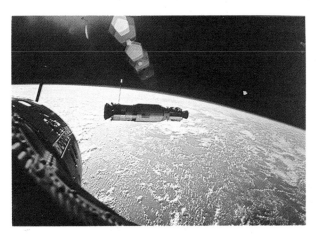

Gemini 10 approaches the unmanned Agena 10 vehicle after catch-up maneuver.

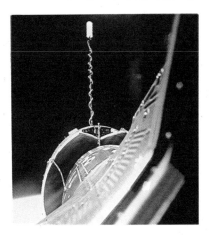

View through command pilot's window moments before docking.

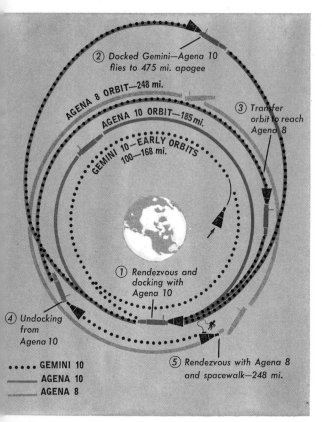

Gemini 10's busy mission in space.

served "red lights" in orbit during their *Gemini 4* mission. Young and Collins had also reported "red lights" near their orbital path just after being placed in orbit. Young radioed to Houston, "I don't think they are stars. We're going right along with them." But the lights disappeared before they could obtain an accurate fix. Although official NASA spokesmen thought the bright objects seen by *Gemini 10* astronauts were remnants of a Saturn test vehicle that had exploded on July 5th, not everyone was satisfied with the Saturn fragments explanation.

There was nothing mysterious or unidentifiable about the one object in space that awaited the *Gemini 10* twins for their last assigned task. This was the silent Agena 8 target which on the third day was within range for rendezvous. Young disengaged from their Agena workhorse and skillfully maneuvered the Gemini craft close enough

for Collins to spacewalk over to the drifting hulk. Carrying a hand-held nitrogen jet gun and tied to Gemini by a 50-foot umbilical cord, Astronaut Collins eased his way to the Agena 8. He detached the micrometeorite impact recorder from the hull and brought it back to Young.

Unfortunately, Collins lost his hand-held camera while outside the capsule and he was too busy with experiments to look for any unknown objects in space. To add to the disappointment, the movie film shot by Young of his companion's spacewalk and the rendezvous with Agena 8 showed only earth and sky with nary a sight of the weightless astronaut floating over to the nearby "dead bird" target vehicle.

After a half hour of EVA (extravehicular activity) Collins was suddenly ordered back to the capsule, ending further experiments in space. Ground controllers back at Houston had become concerned about the astronauts using up their already dangerously low fuel supply. They re-entered the earth's atmosphere the next morning and ended their fine space flight by making a textbook landing within three miles of the recovery ship *Guadalcanal*.

The Command Pilot of *Gemini 10,* John Young, was the co-pilot of the first Gemini flight made in March 1965 with Gus Grissom. Young was born in San Francisco on September 24, 1930 and graduated from Georgia Institute of Technology in 1952 where he received a B.S. degree in aeronautical engineering. After graduation he entered the Navy where he rose through the ranks to Commander. Young set several world jet plane records in 1962 just before entering the astronaut program. These records for climbing speed were made under Project High Jump.

Michael Collins, the pilot of *Gemini 10,* is known in space circles as a doer, not a talker. When he became the first man to crawl out of a space capsule twice in order to view the wonders of space, it was not the first time that he left a flying object. Years before, while participating in Air Force maneuvers near Chambley, France, he had to bail out of a flaming jet. His parachute saved him that day.

Born in Rome, Italy, on October 31, 1930 (the same year as Young), Mike Collins came from a family steeped in military tradition. His father was the late Major General James L. Collins and his uncle, the famed General J. Lawton Collins of World War II. Mike graduated from West Point in 1952 and then took flight training with the Air Force and decided to make that branch of the service his career.

The flight of *Gemini 10* was perhaps the most productive and important manned space experiment to date. It demonstrated man's capabilities to live and work in the hostile atmosphere of space. The mission also established the rudiments of space inspection and proved man's ability to transfer himself from one orbiting body to another. It foreshadowed the landing of men on the moon and showed man's ability to put huge structures together in space. What had been the stuff of science fiction only yesterday was now science fact. Man could now put up orbiting scientific or military laboratories in space, at will. Only time and money would delay him. Still unanswered for many is the nagging mystery of the bright objects that Young and Collins saw several times during their mission.

They left for future astronauts the task of making positive identification of the things that were "too bright for a star."

One day, some astronaut who is as much fascinated with the challenge of space as Collins, will probably find that answer. As Collins described his own motivation: "To get a good, unobscured look at earth, the stars and everything, to perform useful work out there; to me, that's just fascinating in itself."

Artist's rendering shows rendezvous of mated Gemini 10/Agena 10 vehicles with drifting Agena 8 target. The Agena 8 vehicle had been left in space from an earlier abortive Gemini mission.

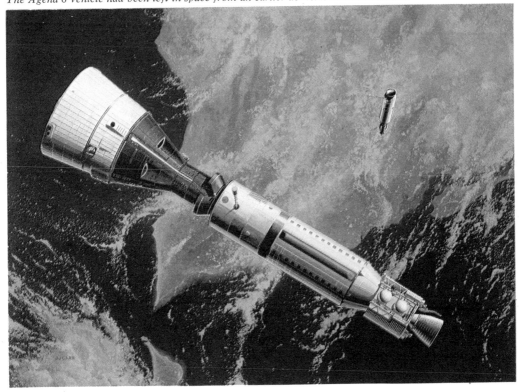

Frank D. Drake

The Father of Project Ozma

The prestigious Space Science Board of the National Academy of Sciences has stated recently that "the most exciting, challenging and profound issue not only of the century, but of the whole naturalistic movement is the search for the existence of intelligent life on other worlds." Many leading space scientists and astronomers feel that the universe is so vast, that the existence of rational life in planetary systems other than our own appears to be more plausible than the alternative assumption that it does not exist.

Such prominent men as Drs. Harold Urey, Philip Morrison, Carl Sagan, Harlow Shapley, Otto Struve and Frank Drake have pushed for closer contacts with our prospective cosmic neighbors. The last of these, Dr. Drake, director of America's first modern attempt to contact life in space, has computed that there may be 10,000,000 extraterrestrial societies within our solar neighborhood, capable of radio communication beyond their own biospheres.

Drake symbolized a different breed of scientist, however, compared with most of the others. As a radio astronomer, he represented new discipline. The young science of radio astronomy dates from 1931, when Karl Jansky discovered that radio waves were coming to the earth from certain stars. When Jansky made his revolutionary discovery of cosmic radio noise, *The New York Times* proclaimed: "Radio Signals from Space Discovered. It Is Believed They Are Not of Intelligent Origin." Even though the headline gave a negative opinion as to the nature of their source, it did show that people were wondering then, over a generation ago, about life on other worlds.

Drake was only one year old at the time of Jansky's announcement, but as he grew up in Chicago, where his father was a chemical engineer, he too became fascinated with the mysteries of the universe. After finishing high school in Chicago, he obtained a scholarship at Cornell. His major there was engineering physics, with an emphasis on mathematics and electronics, but not astronomy. Through the influence of an outstanding Cornell professor, R. W. Shaw, Drake wandered into astronomy via the backdoor elective route.

One other person who helped to inspire Drake was the late Dr. Otto Struve, a Russian born astronomer who fled to the United States following the Bolshevik revolution. Struve made it a habit to always look for the existence of life in space whenever he studied any astronomical data. His Menninger lectures given at Cornell convinced young Drake that astronomy was the field for him. "Over the years, Dr. Struve would continually emphasize that most single, solar-type stars carried planetary systems of their own," Drake reminisced. "Always on his studies of stellar evolution, he would look for indications regarding living things, predicting that there were many, many planetary systems, and a great deal of life in this universe."

After graduation, Drake spent three years in the Navy, where he acquired a well-rounded electronics foundation to go with his astronomy expertise. Upon completion of his naval tour, he enrolled at Harvard in a Ph.D. program centered on astronomy. While there, he built a reputation as a brilliant intellectual who could grasp complex problems quickly. At Harvard's Agassiz radio telescope station, the young, iron-gray haired Drake did some important work on establishing the first clear evidence of the difference between the dark side and the light side temperatures of Venus. Drake's pursuit of scientific advance marked a solitary, but co-operative kind of activity. He helped to forge new links into the never ending chain of discoveries, where one man scrutinizes the findings of others, building upon them with his own interpretation and then relaying it along to the next man.

After graduation from Harvard, Drake found himself one of a group of young radio astronomers, vying for a place in the sun, with no parents to guide him. This new challenging field of astronomy lacked the elder statesmen to give it a sense of balance and maturity. It was a field of largely uncontrolled competition for money and project facilities.

Drake was one of four men who had been working independently in the late fifties on the idea that radio signals might be expected from intelligent beings on other planets. The other three were Dr. Philip Morrison, Dr. Giuseppe Cocconi, and Dr. E. M. Purcell. Upon completion of his doctorate, Drake joined the staff of the National Radio Astronomy Observatory at Green Bank, West Virginia. He was pleased to have a part in helping to put in operation NRAC's spiderweb-like, 85-foot radio antenna, the East's first large radio telescope.

Because of the Maser (Microwave Amplification by Stimulated Emission of Radiation), the new radio telescope had been able to increase the star receiving coverage by a factor of 20,000. This quantum jump in power brought notable results in the initial experiments at Green Bank. Drake made the accidental discovery that the center of the galactic universe was not the single giant star, *Sagittarius A,* as previously believed, but a group of stars instead. In early 1959 Drake also picked up previously undetected emissions from very intense radiation belts encircling Jupiter.

The sensitivity of the new telescope encouraged Drake to secure the necessary support for his own project — that of listening for intelligent signals from outer space. He named his proposal "Project Ozma" after the princess of the imaginary land of Oz. By hitchhiking onto other operating budgets he was able to obtain some 150 hours operating time on the Green Bank "big dish" to explore other star systems for rational life, without the fear of failure haunting him.

"In most of our American scientific institutions," he explained later, "a person's career, his advancement, and his salary depend on concrete results. A good search that fails gets him nothing. He has lost time. He finds himself suddenly losing ground compared with his contemporaries who are getting results, even if they are uninteresting results."

With the aid of a donated parametric, low-noise amplifier and some $2,000 worth of special equipment wangled from Dr. Lloyd V. Berkner, acting director of the observatory, Drake was ready to begin his experiment. According to his reasoning, life could be present on planets revolving around the stars that had remained constant in their intensity for at least five billion years — or similar to our sun. Meeting these requirements were the stars *Tau Ceti* and *Epsilon Eridani.* Convinced that there was a slight chance of making radio contact with these selected target stars on the first try, Drake was stumped as to "what part" of the radio range another highly advanced civilization might be using for transmission.

Because of the excess amount of cosmic noise in the lower frequencies, Drake concluded that the 21 centimeter line of hydrogen appeared to offer the best opportunity for the high sensitivity, narrowbanded widths in which radio telescopes operate. "This is the one striking, natural line in the radio spectrum," he said.

So Drake picked this frequency (1420 megacycles) in which to conduct Project Ozma. He used two receiving horns attached to the telescope's dish, one of which was focused on the target star, and the other aimed away to pick up background noise, so as to obtain a comparison of signals. Although the two celestial targets were the nearest solar-like stars to the earth, Drake knew that it would take at least 11 years for a signal sent from one of them to reach the earth.

He conducted his experiments, beginning in April and ending in June 1959. Starting at 3:30 A.M. he constantly switched the telescope from *Tau Ceti* to *Epsilon Eridani* and then back again, listening to the two stars until late every afternoon, when the telescope would then be used for regular scheduled projects. All the data coming in from *Tau Ceti* and *Epsilon Eridani* was monitored over a loud speaker. The operator waited patiently for three months for a loud or unusual signal but none was heard.

There was one early false alarm, however, in Drake's experiment. It occurred on the first day of the Ozma operation. "Only five minutes after the telescope was turned on to the star *Epsilon Eridani*," he related, "we received an extremely strong signal consisting of about eight bursts of radio noise per second." Before he could double check to confirm that the signal had indeed come from an intelligent civilization or from some earth-based installation, it started fading away and was soon lost entirely.

He made a quick and wise decision to keep the news of the signal secret, because he had been unable to test it. Two weeks later, however, he received the same signal again, but unfortunately it appeared to be stationary, which proved that it was coming from earth. He never did discover its source. (The Naval Research Laboratory confirmed that it, too, had recorded the same signal near Washington, D.C.) This surprise letdown event provided the only excitement during the short span of the project.

Project Ozma was conducted in secret, with no announcement being made even to the scientific community, for fear of receiving undue and unwanted publicity. But on September 19, 1959, Dr. Giuseppe Cocconi, a European nuclear scientist, and Dr. Philip

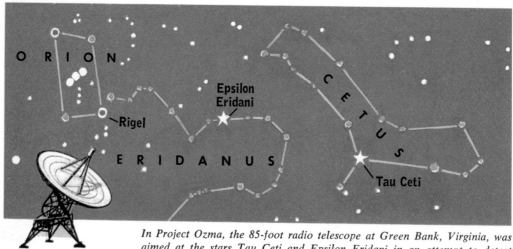

In Project Ozma, the 85-foot radio telescope at Green Bank, Virginia, was aimed at the stars Tau Ceti and Epsilon Eridani in an attempt to detect signals from civilizations in distant space.

Morrison published a paper in the British scientific journal, *Nature,* entitled, "Searching for Interstellar Communications." Their paper contained a suggestion of a search for intelligent space life similar to Ozma's, using the 21 centimeter line of the radio frequency.

When Dr. Otto Struve, who was Director of the NRAO, read the article, he felt it was unfair to those who had originated and conducted the Green Bank experiment. So he made a full disclosure of the Ozma Project in his Compton Lectures delivered a few months later at the Massachusetts Institute of Technology. At last the press discovered Ozma and it became a celebrated, newsworthy item, bringing Drake's name into the headlines.

Once the story of Ozma was known, Drake helped to organize a unique conference on extraterrestrial intelligent life at Green Bank in November 1961. It included a number of experts working in the search for life in space who represented all the major scientific disciplines. By inviting mathematicians, physicists, chemists and biologists, as well as astronomers, the conference broke the narrow departmental confines of those studying the problem. This group discussed informally the prospects for the existence of other societies in our galaxy and the technical problems involved in establishing contact. They agreed on the need of further eavesdropping on a great number of channels with a larger antenna tied to a computer which would store and correlate received data. Drake believes that with a small investment of about $15,000,000, there is a 50% probability of success for an extraterrestrial contact with a stepped-up Ozma-type experiment in 30 years.

Although the Ozma experiment did not impart positive results, it did have a beneficial impact in firing the imagination of others, both in and out of science, to set their sights on an eventual two-way contact with some far-off cosmic civilization. The failure of the Ozma radio astronomers did not rule out the possible continuation of a similar project in the future to contact another star in a different galaxy. If such a contact is made, as it well may in our lifetime, the entire philosophical concept of man's place in the cosmos will be radically changed from that date onward.

In September 1963, Drake left his position as Associate Scientist with the National Radio Astronomy Observatory and went to California where he became Chief of the Lunar and Planetary Sciences Section of the Jet Propulsion Laboratory. In this capacity, he continued to search vigorously for extraterrestrial life.

Although the Green Bank project came up with negative results, it did serve as a catalyst to spur others to seek ways of listening for messages from other rational civilizations in space. Drake, himself, went on to try again to make cosmic contacts, using the huge NASA radio telescope carved out of a mountainside near Arecibo, Puerto Rico. One of these days, he and his colleagues might succeed in their quest.

As Drake put it: "Man is only now emerging from his childhood and preparing to take a place among the community of galactic civilizations that may exist." He still holds his earnest conviction about the existence of intelligent beings in space. "It is statistically certain," he said in conclusion. "Therefore, the search must be conducted. In science, answers are always there to be found."

He was echoing the belief of the Italian inventor of the wireless, Guglielmo Marconi, who in 1921 said that he would expect communciations from another planet to consist of "transmission of pictures accompanied by a simple code." A space TV or radio signal, using basic mathematical symbols, may well become the first contact with intelligent life from other worlds. In this case the contact would take the form of very high or ultra-high frequency invisible signals rather than saucer-shaped visible objects carrying visitors from outer space.

A 14-year-old newspaper boy, Alan Smith, took this night photograph of a UFO that was seen by several other persons on August 2, 1965 over Tulsa, Oklahoma.

74   AMERICA'S EXPLORERS OF SPACE

Special Report on UFO's

Flying Saucer Phenomenon: Mystery in the Sky

For the past 20 years, recurring reports of the sightings of "flying saucers" or "UFO's" (Unidentified Flying Objects) have constituted one of the most perplexing phenomena of our times. Thousands of detailed descriptions of these strange craft have been recorded by various people, but it was not until late 1966 that the U.S. Government took a direct interest in funding an official study to find out just what they were.

Many people, both here and abroad, sincerely believe that these UFO's are really spacecraft manned by visitors from some other world. Such beliefs are by no means limited to the so-called "contactees" who claim that they have visited on these vehicles, or the various crackpot cultists who believe UFO's are flown by demigods. Since many of the sightings have also been reported by reliable, stable people such as policemen, airline pilots, astronomers and citizens possessing considerable intelligence and sophistication, it is no wonder that the public has been confused over the true nature of these objects.

The U.S. Air Force, which has been given the responsibility for checking on any intruders into American air space, has steadfastly claimed up to now that it has no evidence that any craft of other worldly design has penetrated our sovereign skies. The sophisticated space-scanning devices of the North American Air Defense Command (NORAD) have not reported any such objects, although they constantly keep track of over 1,000 items whirling around in space orbit about the earth.

There has been one notable recent exception to this rule, however. Three "unidentified" satellites, which had not been identified "with any launching or country of origin" were discovered by NORAD's spacetrack scanners in May 1966 and were reported in the official government Satellite Situation Report issued on September 30, 1966. This was the first time that the periodic report had listed "unknowns" among the thousand plus satellites, rocket bodies and bits of space debris which are being continuously tracked by the United States. Military officials were fearful at first to release this information to the public because of their apprehension that "flying saucer" enthusiasts would seize upon the term, "unknowns," and cite the objects as evidence of visitors from other worlds.

But their objections were overcome and the objects, which were not inclined to any launching angles used by the Soviet Union, were finally included in the bi-monthly report. The objects were not considered to constitute any military danger to the United States, but still remained "unidentified" six months after their first sighting.

THE AIR FORCE, UFO'S AND PROJECT BLUE BOOK

In the two decades between 1947 and 1966, the U.S. Air Force investigated and analyzed over 11,000 American reports of so-called UFO's, which represented only a fraction of the total global sightings of similar "flying saucers" that occurred during that time span. These sightings have been kept on file in the Air Force's Project Blue Book, which is the official government log of all reported UFO sightings that have been noted over the U.S.A.

The first reported American UFO sighting in the Air Force's Project Blue Book was made by a private pilot, Kenneth Arnold, back on June 24, 1947. He claimed to have seen several moving "things" in the air near Mt. Rainier, Washington. His widely publicized report set off the first modern epidemic-wave of "saucer sightings" that periodically hits the country every few years. Ever since then, the Air Force has been constantly involved in the saucer business.

On April 27, 1949, the Air Force Headquarters issued a statement reflecting its policy at the time: "The mere existence of some yet unidentified flying objects necessitates a constant vigilance on the part of Project Saucer personnel and on the part of the civilian population . . . The saucers are not jokes. Neither are they cause for alarm." Eight months later, the Air Force issued another report entitled "Unidentified Flying Objects — Project Grudge" (December 30, 1949), in which it admitted that if there existed somewhere a celestial body containing a civilization superior to ours, its inhabitants would have a good reason for keeping us under observation. "Such a civilization," the report read, "might observe that on earth we now have atomic bombs and are fast developing rockets. In view of the past history of mankind they should be alarmed. We can, therefore, expect at this time above all to behold such visitations."

When Navy Secretary Dan Kimball tried to get the Office of Naval Research to undertake a separate investigation of UFO's in the spring of 1952 after he and Naval Chief of Staff, Admiral Arthur Radford, spotted two UFO's making passes at their plane on a Pacific tour, he and the Navy struck out when the Air Force refused to co-operate. Interservice rivalry has prevented a sane investigation of UFO's for years.

A few months later, on July 29, 1952, Major General John Samford, the Air Force's Chief of Intelligence, conducted a press conference in Washington in which he admitted that the saucers were "real" and that jet fighters were scrambled when some UFO's were sighted over Washington, D.C. General Samford also spoke of the saucers as "having unlimited power — that means power of such fantastic higher limits that it is theoretically unlimited — it's not anything we can understand." He went on to say that the difficulty in understanding saucers is that history and technology give us "no standard to measure these things by."

The Air Force has set up a series of rigidly enforced regulations concerning the dissemination of information regarding UFO's to the public. Information can be released only if the UFO has been "positively identified as a familiar or known object." Air Force personnel are restricted from discussing UFO's with private citizens except as directed — and then only on a "need-to-know" basis.

In an official Operations and Training Document issued to Air Force personnel on December 24, 1959, headlined — "UFO's — Serious Business," the first paragraph reads: "Unidentified Flying Objects, sometimes treated lightly by the press and referred to as "flying saucers," must be rapidly and accurately identified as serious USAF business." This "business" had become so "serious" that even former Senator Barry Goldwater, a Major General in the Air Force Reserve, said candidly at that time: "The Air Force has a department which investigates UFO's — but if you try to get anything out of them, they clam up!"

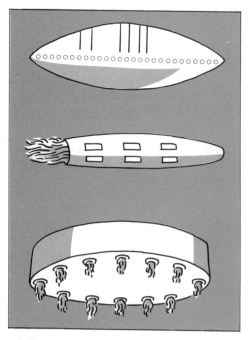

Sketches of unidentified aerial objects based on eyewitness descriptions from U.S. Air Force Blue Book Special Report No. 14.

The original head of Project Blue Book was Capt. Edward J. Ruppelt, who ran the group for two and a half years, until September 1953. After questioning reliable observers of UFO's, such as scientists and pilots, and analyzing hundreds of photos and the radarscope evidence, he changed his original skepticism to a personal conclusion that most of the reports constituted valid sightings, with the most plausible explanation being that UFO's were extraterrestrial. He expressed this view in numerous classified reports to his superiors but was prohibited from stating it publicly. Upon his retirement from the service, however, he published a book entitled, *The Report on Unidentified Flying Objects,* in which he carefully and painstakingly reviewed hundreds of sightings.

In 1965, there were 886 sightings reported to the Air Force. (This figure was topped only by the 1,501 reported in 1951 and the 1,006 in 1957.) It has been estimated that the number of sightings in 1966 was about 900.

The current custodian of Project Blue Book, Major Hector Quintanilla, Jr., a physicist, occupies quarters at the Air Force Research and Development Command, Wright-Patterson Air Force Base in Dayton, Ohio. His functions are threefold: (1) to try to find an explanation for all reported sightings of unidentified flying objects; (2) to discover whether the UFO's pose any security threat; and (3) to determine if the UFO's exhibit any advanced technology which the U.S. could put to use.

The Major is the keeper of a weird collection of bogus hardware items that flying saucer believers have tried to fob off on him as the real thing. One of these alleged cosmic contraptions includes two halves of a crumpled copper shell holding earth-made radio parts. This was passed off as being an extraterrestrial satellite sent to the earth.

To assist Quintanilla, the Air Force has assigned a UFO officer to every air base in the country. This officer initiates an investigation of any sighting in his vicinity.

Project Blue Book continues to check carefully all sightings against the flight paths of known aircraft, balloons and satellites which have been tracked by military and civilian agencies to see if their passes over a certain geographical vicinity coincide with a reported UFO sighting. So far, every errant radar blip that is reported has been accounted for by the Wright-Patterson UFO watchdogs.

Major Quintanilla, who has looked at the records of every UFO case going back to 1947, is firmly convinced that "the vast majority have involved simple misinterpretation of natural phenomena." He has concluded that none of the unidentified sightings that compose the 2% of the total logged in the Blue Book has given any indication of posing a threat to national safety. But he admits that some of the files have remained "open" and the investigation of these sticky UFO's has continued.

Some people believe that there is danger that a UFO might be mistaken by the North American Air Defense Command (NORAD) at Colorado Springs as an enemy missile, thus inadvertently starting World War III. Air Force officials at the Colorado mountain headquarters of NORAD discount this fear, stating that any space object must have a "reflecting surface, be larger than a watermelon and be within radar coverage." So far no UFO sightings have ever been translated into actual saucer hardware unless you count the three "unidentified satellites" sighted by NORAD in May 1966.

The same conclusion has been reached by our Defense Department's global Space Track Network. This highly sensitive array of giant radar dish-antennas can pick up a one square meter target at 2,000 miles. They have never picked up a UFO yet. Neither have our Baker-Nunn space cameras which could photograph a six-inch sphere at the distance of the moon — some 240,000 miles away.

CHARACTERISTICS OF UFO'S

UFO sightings come in all shapes, sizes and colors. According to sighting reports, they fall into several basic categories. The first and most prevalent type is the "saucer" shape. It is usually described as 75 to 100 feet across and edged with lights that blink or change in intensity. The second type with numerous reportings is cigar-shaped with lighted windows usually moving fast in a straight line. A third category would lump all the other shapes which do not resemble the first two basic types. This would include those which are spherical, disc-like, tubular or airplane-like to name just a few. The color range is practically unlimited with red, orange, blue and green predominating.

Among the strange characteristics that seem to repeat themselves with various sightings have been the changing colors of the flashing lights on the objects (which distinguish them from conventional aircraft with their steady, single-color flashing lights), and their amazing ability to execute difficult maneuvers which appear to defy the force of earthly gravity.

Professor Donald Menzel of the Smithsonian Institution, and a former member of the Harvard Observatory, has hypothesized that many of the so-called UFO's that frighten airplane pilots in flight are really "sundogs" — ice crystals that reflect the sunlight in queer shapes. Other explanations of these natural phenomena which have been mistaken for UFO's can be found in linking them up with shooting stars, the visible planets, distant translucent weather balloons, which are bent out of their original globular shape by the high altitude winds and low pressure of the rarefied atmosphere, tracer bullets, debris in the wind, poor photo processes, and artificial earth satellites. (There are now over 35 of these in orbit that can be seen by the naked eye.)

There are also chances that the objects seen are reflections from planes or even birds. In Lubbock, Texas, investigations revealed that birds reflecting light from street lamps may have been responsible for a UFO sighting. This phenomenon is known as "Lubbock Lights." Nature has contributed to the saucer controversy by whipping up unusual saucer-like cloud formations.

NICAP AND THE GROWING UFO CONTROVERSY

Not everyone is in agreement with the explanations just mentioned. One group, strongly critical of what is being done to solve the problem of UFO's, is the National Investigation Committee on Aerial Phenomena. NICAP, as it is known, is directed by Donald E. Keyhoe, a retired marine major and former pilot. The headquarters for this loosely knit, non-governmental and non-profit organization are in Washington, D.C. Its membership of 5,000 UFO buffs includes hundreds of technicians and a number of retired military officers who believe that the objects of their joint interest are "manifestations of extraterrestrial life." In NICAP's privately printed volume entitled, *The UFO Evidence,* published in 1964, some 746 UFO sightings are listed with brief accompanying descriptions of date, place, name(s) of the person(s) who observed the phenomena and sketches or photos where available. None of their documented sightings offer any evidence of humanoid extraterrestrial visitors either landing on earth or being spotted aboard the UFO's, but NICAP has provided an unclassified chronology of major U.S. sightings made over the past two decades.

The Board of Governors of NICAP includes the former head of the Central Intelligence Agency and several prominent, retired admirals and generals. This civilian UFO watchdog organization has staunchly maintained that the U.S. Air Force "has practiced an intolerable degree of secrecy, keeping the public in the dark about the amount and possible significance of UFO evidence."

Admiral R. H. Hillenkoetter, one of NICAP's charter members, who formerly commanded the CIA, stated bluntly in the spring of 1966: "Behind the scenes, high-ranking Air Force officers are soberly concerned about the UFO's but through official secrecy and ridicule, many citizens are led to believe the unknown flying objects are nonsense . . . To hide the fact, the Air Force has silenced its personnel . . . It is time for the truth to be brought out in open Congressional hearings."

Dr. J. Allen Hynek, who is the Air Force's chief civilian UFO investigator, has stated: "There is no valid scientific proof that we have been visited by outer-space-ships. The IFO (Identified Flying Objects) have been the usual things seen under unusual circumstances, i.e., meteorological balloons, meteors, etc., but there is a residue of unexplained sightings." He told a Congressional investigating committee in April 1966, that he, personally, was convinced that there had been "no invasion from outer space." As a scientist, however, he tries to keep an open mind about the extraterrestrial theory as "one possible hypothesis."

Dr. Hynek has noted that most UFO reports do not originate with persons who believe in outer space visitations, but from solid citizens. "I regard our 'Unidentifieds' as a blot on our escutcheon," he confessed. "Somehow we scientists should be able to come up with answers for these things."

Major Quintanilla, although certain that no evidence turned up to date has even hinted at spacecraft of unearthly origin, agreed that "It is impossible to prove that flying saucers do not exist." Then he posed a hopeful thought: "We are spending millions to develop our own rocket boosters to get our spacecraft to the moon and beyond. Imagine what a great help it would be to get our hands on a ship from another planet and examine its power plant."

While NICAP agrees that 80% of the UFO sightings have been "honest mistakes," they are disillusioned with the "inadequate job" performed by the Air Force on the other 20% where at least "one new impressive case" crops up every week. Donald Keyhoe, NICAP's Director, accused the Air Force of playing "dirty pool" with the American public on the subject.

Lt. Colonel Lawrence Tacker, Air Force Public Relations Officer, has stated unequivocally that the charges made by NICAP

Atmospheric distortion of common phenomena could account for many UFO reports.

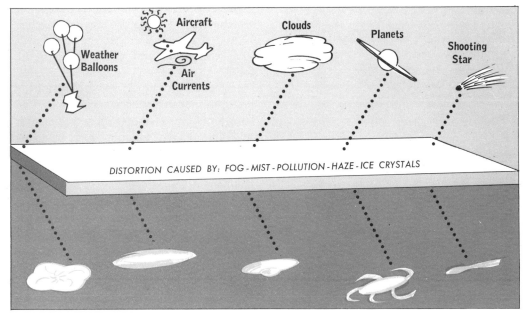

The UFO's pictured below show marked similarity. The one at the top was photographed in 1950 in Oregon, and its close twin was observed in France four years later.

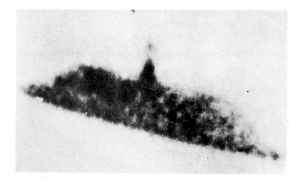

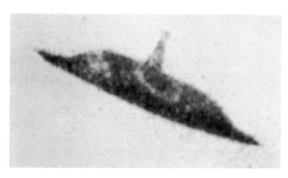

UFO photographed by an officer aboard the S.S. Ramsey off the coast of California in 1957.

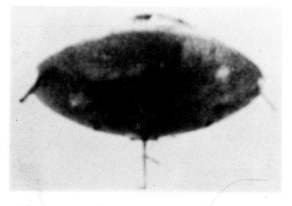

and others against the Air Force are "untrue." "We are not withholding information. There is nothing in the Air Force classified or unclassified files that show spaceships from some other planet have visited earth." He admitted, however, that 659 of the reported 11,000 sightings kept in the Wright-Patterson Air Force Base (Ohio) files are still "unidentified."

RECENT UFO SIGHTINGS

The latest series of dramatic UFO sightings in the skies above America occurred over a nine-month period from midsummer 1965 to the early spring of 1966. On August 1, 1965, the authorities in eight western states were deluged with dozens of UFO reports. The Oklahoma Highway Patrol reported that police officers in three patrol cars had watched some celestial objects, flying in a diamond-shaped formation for 30 minutes. They changed in color from red to white to blue to green. Nearby Tinker Air Force Base reported that it was tracking as many as four of the objects on its radar screen.

The next day the Air Force announced authoritatively that what hundreds of people had reported seeing was really only the planet Jupiter or the stars Rigel, Capella, or Aldebaran. They did not comment on the Kansas Weather Bureau's radar observations which reported tracking several of the UFO's at altitudes of from 6,000 to 9,000 feet. The Air Force explanation was promptly debunked by Robert Risser, the Director of the Oklahoma Planetarium, who told reporters that watchers in his state certainly did not see the planet or the stars listed by the Air Force. "That is as far from the truth as you can get," he stated. "These stars are on the opposite side of the earth from Oklahoma at this time of year!"

Three weeks later, on August 21, 1965, the conservative *Christian Science Monitor* published an article in which its science editor discussed some apparently authentic photos made of the Oklahoma UFO's and charged the Air Force with "trying to brush off UFO reports."

Two weeks later another peculiar UFO sighting occurred. In the early morning hours of September 3, 1965, Norman Muscarello, a Navy enlistee, witnessed an 80- to 90-foot long object hovering close to the earth near Exeter, New Hampshire, just north of the Massachusetts state line.

The Exeter report was interesting not only because it was listed on the official records of the local police, including its verification by two reliable police officers, but it was also noted by five other local people who observed the object at altitudes ranging from 20 to 100 feet during the same night. Many said they saw red pulsating lights around the UFO's rim, which often would speed up and whirl. Some noted cigar-shaped spacecrafts.

A number of observers said that when they saw the Exeter UFO, the "thing" was not more than five or six feet off the ground. Most reported absolute silence by the objects, but a few noticed a high-frequency hum, which was connected with simultaneous electrical, ignition, and radio broadcast

disturbances. Other observers reported the hovering objects near high-power transmission lines and claimed that they caused a violent reaction in dogs and cattle.

A recent critical research study of the Exeter and other sightings by Phillip Klass, a physicist, caused him to reach the conclusion that most of these UFO phenomena were really ion plasmas or ball lightning. Klass, who is the Avionics Editor of the authoritative technical journal, *Aviation Week and Space Technology,* theorized that these luminous plasmas, also known as "kugelblitz," are usually found near high-tension, electric power lines and are related to the phenomenon known as St. Elmo's fire.

When a UFO appeared over a swamp located on the land of a 47-year-old Michigan farmer, Frank Mannor, in February 1966, his neighbors called him a "nut" after he described the silent, hovering object to them. Subsequent events made many of them wonder whether the father of ten children wasn't sane after all. On the night of March 21st, William Van Horn, the Civil Defense Director of nearby Hillsdale County, was called to the dormitory of

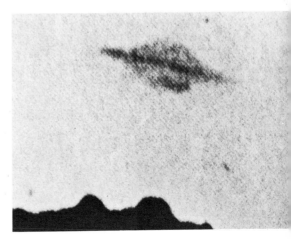

Several witnesses aboard the Brazilian Navy research vessel Almirante Saldanha saw this UFO as it zoomed over the tiny island Trindade in the South Atlantic.

Hillsdale College where, along with a group of girl students, he watched a "flashing object from the northeast."

On March 24th, the Air Force hinted that it would have a rational explanation of the southern Michigan swamp sightings within 24 hours. After the Air Force sent their ace consultant investigator, Dr. J. Allen Hynek of Northwestern University, to look into the sightings, the bearded astronomer quickly came up with the conclusion that they were nothing but "swamp light"— balls of swamp gas released by the spring thaws that floated away on the wind. This phenomenon is known in folklore as "will o' the wisp" and the "jack-o-lantern." "A dismal swamp is a most unlikely place for a visit from outer space," Hynek said.

Civil Defense Director Van Horn didn't accept Hynek's Air Force report. A month and a half later, on May 16th, he issued a 24-page report refuting the "swamp gas" explanation by listing wind tables which indicated that there was too much wind that night for swamp gas to form. He also charged that Hynek issued a quickie report, spending less than three hours in his investigation, compared to Van Horn's seven-week research. Van Horn also concluded that the average monthly temperatures proved that swamp gas could not form under existing conditions.

The explanation of the Michigan sightings was also not good enough for Donald Keyhoe, Director of NICAP, who believed that the Air Force was hiding the real truth behind this and other similar sightings.

CONGRESS MOVES INTO THE MELEE

When the UFO rationale of the Michigan sightings was released, many members of a suspicious Congress were not ready to accept the Air Force's simple explanation of "swamp gas" as the final answer to the problem. But a vexed and perplexed Congress was reluctant to investigate the situation, since to do so would encourage the idea that there was more to UFO's than

mistaken sightings of natural and man-made objects. On the other hand, a refusal to investigate would leave Congress open to the charge that the Government knew what the saucers were but was merely trying to "cover up" their true identity from the people. Others feared that a "full-blown investigation might frighten much of the public, no matter what findings resulted."

One spokesman of the House Armed Services Committee even suggested that the House Committee on Un-American Activities should investigate the saucer sightings because "it is un-American to have unidentified objects flying over this country." But the rest of the committee agreed that it shouldn't laugh at those who said they had seen saucers. "That might be like laughing at the guy who thought of the submarine for the first time," one member said.

Even the Air Force half-heartedly said that it still welcomed "any evidence of the existence and intraspace mobility of extraterrestrial life," particularly if it was "operating within the earth's near-space envelope."

During the same week that the UFO's were sighted in Hillsdale, Michigan, John King, a 22-year-old Bangor, Maine, man said he shot four times at a 60-foot-long glowing object and hit it. Then it zoomed skyward. "I could hear the elderberry bushes scraping as the thing came toward me," King said.

During the same late March period, a postman in Colorado, a newsman in Wisconsin, and an Air Force electronics instructor in Oklahoma all reported seeing mysterious celestial objects. The electronics man said a "fish-shaped craft manned by an 'ordinary human'" blocked his car near the Texas border. In Texas, police reported hundreds of people had called in saying that they had seen a starlike object that "purred and changed colors."

On March 28th, the civilian NICAP group challenged the government to release all information it had on UFO's. "There is

Lens flare or UFO's — this picture showing strange objects was taken by photographer-seaman S. Alpert at the Coast Guard's Salem, Massachusetts, air station on July 16, 1952.

substantial evidence we are being observed by some sort of device which is far more advanced than anything we have and is controlled by a superior civilization," said Donald Keyhoe, NICAP Director, at a news conference. The retired Marine officer continued, "These things are real and under intelligent control. I urge the Air Force to end the secrecy of sightings and stop ridiculing competent witnesses."

On March 30, 1966, the Air Force staunchly claimed that it still maintained an open mind about UFO's. An official Pentagon spokesman denied that the Air Force tried to squelch UFO reports. "In the first place, we'd be utterly foolish to try to keep people from telling about something they've seen with their own eyes. Our job is to explain what is seen, not necessarily to change anybody's mind."

But many critics were not buying this rationale, especially three weeks later, when the Air Force explained that the latest UFO sightings over Ohio were nothing more than a "combination of an artificial satellite and the planet Venus."

Two Ohio deputy sheriffs swore that what they had seen couldn't be either of these official military explanations, since they knew that the artificial earth satellites didn't come that close to earth. They claimed that they followed a "bright, circular" UFO about 45 feet in diameter for 85 miles along a highway from Atwater, Ohio, to Freedom, Pa., about 5 A.M. on April 17th. According to the two policemen, the bright object appeared to be no more than 1,000 feet in the air. And so the UFO controversy raged on.

In early April 1966, the Air Force reported that it wasn't really worried about the recent rash of unexplained flying saucer reports but, just in case, Air Force Secretary, Dr. Harold Brown, assured the House Armed Services Committee that he would

83

probably ask some outside scientific experts to take another look at the mysterious sightings. Brown also noted that a civilian Air Force advisory group had recommended a month earlier further intensive study by a university or non-profit scientific organization of the over 500 unexplained UFO reports. This group mildly chided the Air Force for listing some sightings as "identified" where "the evidence collected was too meager or too indefinite to permit positive listing."

The scientific advisory board had suggested in March that each university team should include at least one psychologist, preferably one interested in clinical psychology, and at least one physical scientist (probably an astronomer or geophysicist familiar with atmospheric physics).

Brown's Congressional testimony ended the chances of a full-scale Congressional investigation into UFO's, for the time being, as requested by House Minority Leader Ford. Brown told the committee, headed by Rep. L. Mendel Rivers (Dem., S.C.), that the Air Force's UFO investigations had explained satisfactorily all but 10% of the flying saucer reports it had received.

He claimed that marsh gas, pranks, planets, comets, meteors, fireballs, and auroral streamers had caused most of the reports of the strange, bright objects in the sky. Brown assured the Congress that there was no reason to believe that any of the unexplained sightings represented either security threats, extraterrestrial vehicles or any development "beyond present day scientific knowledge."

It wasn't until over three months later, however, that Brown finally acted on his UFO advisory group's recommendation, when his office announced on July 14th that the Air Force intended to make several contracts with a few selected universities to provide scientific teams "to investigate promptly and in depth" sightings of UFO's.

It was obvious that the Air Force was reacting to the pressure for action building up by American public opinion. This pressure was ignited not only by the sightings in the spring of 1966 but by the calls of NICAP and various responsible authors of contemporary books on the UFO phenomena for a more thorough investigation of the objects.

The results of the first national public opinion sampling on the issue, taken by Dr. George Gallup, showed that the nation also took the UFO sightings seriously. He estimated that more than five million Americans had seen objects called "flying saucers" according to a poll released on May 8, 1966. Furthermore, he concluded that an estimated 50 million American people would say, if asked, that they believe these "UFO's are real." This meant that

Dr. J. Allen Hynek

Donald E. Keyhoe

Dr. Edward U. Condon

one out of two adult Americans believed that saucers were a fact and not the figment of one's imagination!

Unfortunately for its popular image, the Air Force did not think of the UFO's as serious business until public and Congressional pressure forced them to change their posture in mid-1966.

Because the Air Force officialdom and the bulk of their scientific advisors seemed to agree on the improbability of the so-called flying saucers being populated by visitors from other planets, the rationale for this consistent attitude was rather obvious. The military service's skepticism on the possibilities of extraterrestrial contacts with the earth led them to seek other types of explanations for the UFO sightings. The professional skepticism was largely due to the limited number of persons making any one sighting, coupled with the lack of any undeniable physical evidence such as scorched grass, a print on the ground or a piece of UFO hardware.

THE AIR FORCE CONTRACTS FOR A STUDY OF UFO'S

The U.S. Air Force, at the request of its Director of Information, and not its military or intelligence elements, finally, in early October 1966, took a sound step to overcome the charges that it considered past reports of UFO's to have a predominantly psychiatric rather than an aerodynamic basis. It announced that the distinguished physicist, Dr. Edward U. Condon, who is noted for speaking his mind, had agreed to serve as a scientific director for a far-ranging, no-strings UFO inquiry backed by $313,000 of Air Force money.

The study contract for the investigation was to last 18 months, and could be extended, if necessary. It would be centered at the University of Colorado in Boulder and would involve psychologists as well as men like Condon, who was a prominent astrophysicist there. The Air Force assured the university investigators that they would provide all the information that they possessed on the subject of UFO's to help them with their research. This move marked the first step to bring recognized scientists into the muddled UFO picture so that they might help to unravel the mystery.

THE RELATIONSHIP OF UFO'S TO EXTRATERRESTRIAL LIFE

The British, Brazilian and Canadian governments are known to have UFO observation and analyzing offices working on the phenomena, but like the U.S. Air Force, most of their reports are cloaked in official government secrecy. British Air Force Historian, Gibbs Smith of the London Museum, fully believes that 5% of the UFO sightings are from outside of our solar system. "We forget we are a fifth-rate lot of apes," he said. "We are all thinking medievally. Descriptions do not fit any other explanation."

Many popular theories have been put forth in recent times to explain the origin of UFO's. M .M. Agrest thought that there had been extraterrestrial visitation of the earth in prehistoric times and that such visitation was now being repeated. Paul Misraki worked on the hypothesis that there is extraterrestrial intervention in man's religion. Carl Sagan theorized that the moon might be a relay base for creatures from another solar system. At the present time the most plausible explanation seems to be the one presented by Oberth.

Professor Hermann Oberth is the former German rocket scientist and teacher of Dr. Wernher von Braun, a staunch member of NICAP and a believer that the government knows where the "flying saucers" come from and what they are up to. He made his extraterrestrial hypothesis statement back in 1958. Oberth believed that the UFO's come from two stars, *Tau Ceti* and *Epsilon Eridani,* located about 11 light years away. Strangely enough, these were the same two stars picked as targets by Dr. Frank Drake during his famous Project Ozma radio telescopic listening experiment for radio signs of extraterrestrial life.

In view of the recent history of UFO sightings, more credence has been put on the estimates by some of our leading astronomers that we are being observed by extraterrestrial civilizations. Former Harvard Astronomer, Harlow Shapley has estimated that one solar system in a million probably supports intelligent forms of life — out of the 50 billion solar systems in our galaxy. Carl Sagan is less conservative. He computes the ratio at one in 100,000. Whatever the correct figures, modern scientific opinion is now nearly unanimous that the known universe contains millions of technologically oriented civilized societies, with some undoubtedly being more advanced than our own.

Some may even have been able to break through the light barrier and build devices that can travel faster than the speed of light — 186,000 miles per second. Most of our present day scientists say that such speeds are impossible to achieve. But just 20 years ago, many responsible scientists were saying that man would never break the sound barrier of a puny 700 m.p.h. — until Col. Charles Yeager accomplished this historic feat in 1947.

Because some of these UFO's may be traveling *faster* than the speed of light when they so quickly disappear from view, after hovering at rather slow speeds, we thus are presented with a possible rational explanation for the inability of the human viewer to comprehend why the celestial object he was watching suddenly vanishes. This may be one important key to unlock the mysteries of those UFO's which are still unaccounted for and are attributed to hallucinations on the part of the viewers.

It is possible that extraterrestrial molecular particles traveling *faster* than the speed of light may make it biologically impossible for us to communicate with any rational forms of life that might be accompanying the object. Furthermore, they could be so far above us in their thinking patterns as to preclude any intelligent contact.

In the NICAP's lengthy 1964 report, there appeared a letter from Dr. Clyde Tombaugh, the noted astronomer, discoverer of the planet Pluto, and presently chief of the Armed Services search for natural satellites. He described a sighting observed by both his wife and himself as follows: "These things, which do appear to be directed, are unlike any other phenomena, I ever observed. Other stars in our galaxy may have hundreds of thousands of inhabited worlds. Races on these worlds may have been able to utilize the tremendous amounts of power required to bridge the space between the stars."

According to some members of NICAP, who were themselves once a part of the inner sanctum of the U.S. government, bitter arguments have continued to rage at the highest levels between the so-called "silence group" and the "open door group" who feel that the public should know the truth about the UFO's. NICAP maintains that at one time in the pre-Sputnik era, there was an official government plan to leak and release saucer information by degrees to the public so as not to "cause a panic."

The Pentagon actually did clear one article back in 1950. It was written by a Commander R. B. McLaughlin, who told in detail how his crew of scientists, as well as other scientists, carefully tracked several disc-shaped UFO's at White Sands Proving Grounds, New Mexico. He was convinced that the "flying saucers" seen traveling at 25,200 m.p.h. at 296,000 feet were "spaceships from another planet operated by animate, intelligent beings."

By 1953, according to NICAP, the "silence group" won out in the internal Pentagon power struggle, and such press conferences or officially cleared articles by military personnel on the subject of extraterrestrial "visitations" were no longer publicized openly.

In late May 1966, a group of American space scientists, meeting at the Disneyland Hotel in Anaheim, California, held a symposium on the theme: "The Search for Extraterrestrial Life." Conducted under the auspices of the American Astronautical Society, the authoritative panel discussions offered convincing arguments that there was intelligent life in space, with a good chance of earthmen contacting it in the next few decades. Many of the speakers and 300 scientists present admitted that the topic would have seemed bizarre if discussed a few years earlier. But times have changed, and scientific facts have suddenly become wilder than most science fiction. Today's conjecture may become tomorrow's reality.

Dr. Bernard Oliver, a Vice President of the Hewlett-Packard Co., urged the nation to embark immediately on a $3-to-$5 million American program for antennas and receiving systems covering a 100-square-mile area for exchanging messages with life on other planets.

Dr. Frank Drake felt that it would be possible "to achieve a high probability of radio contact with another intelligent civilization within a 30-year period" if we embarked upon an intensive "search" program. He noted that a similar group "of the most prominent Soviet scientists in the Soviet Union had just taken the position that the detection of extraterrestrial civilization would be of such profound significance that the expensive search should be undertaken even though success cannot be guaranteed."

He noted that his lack of guarantee that such life exists has been the inhibiting factor that has stalled a massive government-backed program from getting underway in either country. It is up to the scientists, Drake said, to increase public confidence in the strong possibilities of such life.

At the same conference, Harold Lasswell, a Professor of Political Science and Law at Yale University, noted that sudden contact between the earth and a civilization that was at a far more advanced techno-scientific level could have a cataclysmic impact upon our society. He predicted that there would be a sharp impulse for our society to discard its traditional values, and that a "cult of despair would develop."

Man's self image would undergo a "profound transformation" as earth creatures attempted to "remodel" themselves along the line of the newly encountered superior culture, he concluded. But does this dire future event have to occur, one might ask? If mature men can be educated to believe in the existence of such cosmic cultures, then when *that* day arrives when the first extraterrestrial contact is made, the shock might not be as great as that caused by the first Sputnik or the atomic bomb dropped over Hiroshima.

Man *can* and *must* plan now to cushion himself for the impact of the revolutionary changes that will sweep over the earth when he first detects life out there.

When that day arrives, a combination of both visual and audio communications can most probably be established between the predominantly silent UFO's and their earth observers. Chances are that some ultra-high frequency wave length may be used to talk with UFO's. It would be beyond the pitch of normal human hearing capabilities, but could be recorded and translated by sensitive electronic computer instruments.

Many space scientists now believe that "God's quarantine" of the great distance in light years between solar systems practically guarantees that the first contact with another civilization will be via audio-radio contact rather than a visual UFO one.

No matter how that initial contact is made, we need to re-assess our philosophy concerning America's place in both the world and the universe. An international dialogue ought to be started soon, encompassing ideas of various professions coming from different space-faring powers. This may be the single, most important legacy of the impact of the UFO's.

Chronology of U.S. Manned Space Flights

Launch Date	Astronaut(s)	Spacecraft Name	Flight Time (hours/minutes)	No. of Orbits & Max. Height	Remarks
5/5/61	Alan B. Shepard Jr.	Mercury Freedom 7	15 m	Suborbital 116 mi.	First U.S. manned space flight
7/21/61	Virgil I. Grissom	Mercury Liberty Bell 7	16 m	Suborbital 118 mi.	Second American in space
2/20/62	John H. Glenn Jr.	Mercury Friendship 7	4 h 55 m	3 orbits 162.7 mi.	First U.S. manned orbital space flight
5/24/62	M. Scott Carpenter	Mercury Aurora 7	4 h 56 m	3 orbits 166.8 mi.	Initiated research experiments in space
10/3/62	Walter M. Schirra Jr.	Mercury Sigma 7	9 h 13 m	6 orbits 176 mi.	Prolonged duration of weightlessness
5/15/63	L. Gordon Cooper Jr.	Mercury Faith 7	34 h 20 m	22 orbits 166.1 mi.	Last and longest Mercury flight
3/23/65	Virgil I. Grissom John W. Young	Gemini 3	4 h 54 m	3 orbits 140 mi.	First U.S. 2-man space flight
6/3/65	James A. McDivitt Edward H. White II	Gemini 4	97 h 59 m	62 orbits 182 mi.	First "spacewalk" (EVA) by White
8/21/65	L. Gordon Cooper Jr. Charles Conrad Jr.	Gemini 5	190 h 56 m	100 orbits 219 mi.	Broke Soviet endurance record
12/4/65	Frank Borman James A. Lovell Jr.	Gemini 7	330 h 35 m	206 orbits 210 mi.	World's longest manned flight
12/15/65	Walter M. Schirra Jr. Thomas P. Stafford	Gemini 6	25 h 51 m	100 orbits 168 mi.	First successful space rendezvous
3/16/66	Neil A. Armstrong David R. Scott	Gemini 8	10 h 42 m	11 orbits 185 mi.	First space docking; aborted flight
6/3/66	Thomas P. Stafford Eugene A. Cernan	Gemini 9	72 h 21 m	45 orbits 144 mi.	Practice rendezvous and 2-hour EVA
7/18/66	John W. Young Michael Collins	Gemini 10	70 h 46 m	43 orbits 475 mi.	Double rendezvous; height record; EVA
9/12/66	Charles Conrad Jr. Richard F. Gordon Jr.	Gemini 11	71 h 17 m	44 orbits 850 mi.	Orbital spin, new height record; EVA
11/11/66	James A. Lovell Jr. Edward E. Aldrin Jr.	Gemini 12	94 h 27 m	59 orbits 460 mi.	Final Gemini flight, most successful EVA
Early 1968	Walter M. Schirra Jr. Walter Cunningham Donn F. Eisele	Apollo 2	14 days (planned)		First manned flight of 3-man Apollo craft

Further Reading

EXPLORERS OF SPACE

Clarke, Arthur C., *Man and Space.* Time Inc., New York, 1964

Daugherty, Charles M., *Robert Goddard.* Macmillan Co., New York, 1964

Epstein, Beryl and Williams, Frank, *Rocket Pioneers on the Road to Space.* Putnam, New York, 1955

Mallan, Lloyd, *Men, Rockets and Space Rats.* Julian Messner Inc., New York, 1961

Sullivan, Walter, *We Are Not Alone.* McGraw-Hill, New York, 1966

Thomas, Shirley, *Men of Space* (Vols. 1–7). Chilton Books, Philadelphia, 1960–1965

Walters, Helen B., *Wernher von Braun: Rocket Engineer.* Macmillan Co., New York, 1964

NASA, *A Walk in Space.* National Aeronautics and Space Administration, Washington, D.C., 1963

NASA, *First United States Manned Orbital Space Flight.* National Aeronautics and Space Administration, Washington, D.C., 1962

UNIDENTIFIED FLYING OBJECTS

Adamski, George and Leslie, D., *Flying Saucers Have Landed.* London House & Maxwell, New York, 1953

Edwards, Frank, *UFO's, Serious Business.* Lyle Stuart Inc., New York, 1966

Fuller, John G., *Incident at Exeter.* Putnam, New York, 1966

Keyhoe, Donald E., *Flying Saucers From Outer Space.* Holt, Rinehart & Winston, New York, 1953

Ruppelt, Edward J., *The Report on Unidentified Flying Objects.* Doubleday & Co., New York, 1956

Vallee, Jacques, *Anatomy of a Phenomenon.* Henry Regnery Co., Chicago, 1965

LIFE, O'Neill, Paul, *A Well-Witnessed Invasion by Something.* April 1, 1966

LOOK, Special by Editors of UPI and Cowles Communications, Inc., *Flying Saucers.* 1967

LOOK, Fuller, John G., *Outer Space Ghost Story.* February 22, 1966

PAGEANT, Tyler, Stephen, *Why the Air Force Hides the Truth About Flying Saucers.* July 1966

SATURDAY REVIEW, Lear, John, *What Are the Unidentified Aerial Objects?* August 6, 1966

THIS WEEK, Nebel, Long John, *But I Tell You I Saw It.* May 15, 1966

UNITED STATES AIR FORCE, *Special Report 14* (Project Blue Book). U.S. Government Printing Office, Washington, D.C., 1954

Glossary

ABORT: To cut short or break off an action, operation, or procedure with an aircraft, space vehicle, or the like, especially because of equipment failure.

APOGEE: In an orbit about the earth, the point at which the satellite is farthest from the earth; the highest altitude reached by a sounding rocket.

ASTRONAUTICS: The art, skill, or activity of operating space vehicles. In a broader sense, the science of space flight.

ATTITUDE: The position or orientation of an aircraft, spacecraft, etc., either in motion or at rest, as determined by the relationship between its axes and some reference line such as the horizon.

BALLISTIC TRAJECTORY: The trajectory followed by a body being acted upon only by gravitational forces and the resistance of the medium through which it passes.

BOOSTER ROCKET: A rocket engine, using either solid or liquid fuel, that assists the normal propulsive system or sustainer engine of a rocket or aeronautical vehicle.

CENTRIFUGE: Specifically, a large motor-driven apparatus with a long arm at the end of which human and animal subjects or equipment can be revolved and rotated at various speeds to simulate accelerations encountered in rockets, high-speed aircraft, and spacecraft.

COMMUNICATIONS SATELLITE: A satellite designed to reflect or relay electromagnetic signals used for communication.

CONTROL ROCKET: A vernier engine, retro-rocket, or other such rocket, used to change the attitude of, guide, or make small changes in the speed of a spacecraft.

CUT-OFF: An act or instance of shutting something off; specifically, in rocketry, an act of shutting off the propellant flow or combustion in a rocket.

DOCKING: The process of bringing two spacecraft together while in space.

DROGUE PARACHUTE: A type of parachute used to slow an object down; also called deceleration parachute or drag parachute.

EVA: Extra Vehicular Activity, the technical term for "space walking."

EXPLOSIVE BOLT: A bolt incorporating an explosive which can be detonated on command.

G or g: An acceleration equal to the acceleration of gravity, approximately 32.2 feet per second per second at sea level; used as a unit of stress measurement for bodies undergoing acceleration.

HEAT SHIELD: The protective structure necessary to protect a re-entry body from aerodynamic heating.

HYPERGOLIC: Propellants, fuel, and oxidizer, which ignite spontaneously upon contact; hydrazine and nitrogen tetroxide are examples.

MACH NUMBER: A way of expressing high speeds relative to the speed of sound in the surrounding air. MACH 1 is the speed of sound.

MASER: (Microwave amplification by stimulated emission of radiation): A device which utilizes the natural oscillations of an atomic or molecular system for amplifying or producing electromagnetic waves.

ORBIT: The path of a body or particle under the influence of a gravitational or other force. For instance, the orbit of a satellite is its path relative to another body around which it revolves.

OXIDIZER: Specifically, a substance (not necessarily containing oxygen) that supports the combustion of a fuel or propellant.

PERIGEE: Position of a satellite in orbit around earth when it is closest to the earth.

PITCH: The movement of an aircraft or spacecraft about its lateral (nose going up or down) axis.

PRESSURE SUIT: A garment designed to provide pressure upon the body so that respiratory and circulatory functions may continue normally under low-pressure conditions, such as occur at high altitude or in space without benefit of a pressurized cabin.

PROPELLANT: Any agent used for combustion in a rocket and from which the rocket derives its thrust.

RADIO ASTRONOMY: The study of celestial objects through observation of radio frequency waves emitted or reflected by these objects.

RADIO TELESCOPE: A radio receiver-antenna combination used for observations in radio astronomy.

REACTION ENGINE: An engine that develops thrust by expelling a jet or stream of gases or fluids.

RE-ENTRY: The event occurring when a spacecraft or other object comes back into the atmosphere after being rocketed into space.

REGENERATIVE COOLING: The cooling of a part of an engine by the fuel or propellant being delivered to the combustion chamber.

RETROROCKET: A rocket fitted on or in a spacecraft, satellite, or the like to produce thrust opposed to forward motion.

ROLL: The rotational movement of an aircraft or similar body which takes place about a longitudinal axis through the body.

SENSOR: A device designed to respond to heat, cold, light or particular motion and convert that response into a signal to be recorded or acted upon.

SOLAR BATTERY: A device consisting of one or more photovoltaic cells which convert sunlight into electrical energy.

SUBORBITAL: Non-orbiting or ballistic flight trajectory from launch point to target point.

TELEMETRY: The technique of collecting scientific and operational data from a rocket or spacecraft in flight and transmitting such data to a distant station for recording, interpreting, etc.

VAN ALLEN RADIATION BELT (For James A. Van Allen, 1915–   .): The zone of high-intensity radiation surrounding the earth.

WEIGHTLESSNESS: The condition that occurs in free flight above the atmosphere when gravity is neutralized. The gravitational force is in balance with the inertia imparted to the vehicle.

YAW: The lateral rotational or oscillatory movement of an aircraft, rocket, or the like about a transverse axis.

ZERO-G: State of complete weightlessness.

Index

Abort switch, 51
Aerodynamics, 18
Aerojet Engineering Co.
 (now Aerojet General Corp.), 20
Agassiz Radio Telescope
 Station, 71
Agena (satellite), 66,67
Agena/Atlas (rocket), 66
Air Force Flight Test Center, 25
Air Force Scientific Advisory
 Group, 21
Aldebaran (star), 80
American Astronautical
 Society, 87
American Rocket Society,
 14,15,29,35,57
American Telephone and
 Telegraph Co., 35
Apogee, 67
Apollo I (capsule), 45,53,61
Apollo (spacecraft), 33
Apollo program, 41,45,58,64
Army Ballistic Missile Agency,
 30,31,54
Arnold, General Henry H., 20–21
Arnold, Kenneth, 75
Astounding Science-Fiction
 (journal), 35
Astronautical Federation, Int'l, 57
Astroprimate, 47
Atlas (rocket), 46,48
*Aviation Week and Space
 Technology*, 81

B–29 (launch plane), 22
Baker-Nunn space cameras, 77
Bell Aircraft, 22
Bell Telephone Laboratories, 34
Bell X–1, 17
Berkner, Lloyd V., 71
Black Betsy (rocket engine), 17
Boushey, Captain Homer, 20
Braun, Wernher von, 13,30–33,
 54,85
Brown, Harold, 83
Brucker, Wilber, 30
Bull, Harry W., 15

Canaveral, Cape (Cape Kennedy),
 30,32,36,38,42,43,45,46,47,49,
 51,61
Canister, lithium hydroxide, 67
Cap Com, 42,52
Capella (star), 80
Card File 23 (radio relay plane),
 43
Carpenter, Scott, 47
Central Control Blockhouse, 40
Chaffee, Roger, 45,53,61
Christian Science Monitor, 80
Clark University, Worcester,
 Mass., 10
Clarke, Arthur, 34
Cocconi, Giuseppe, 71
Collins, Michael, 66–69
Colorado, University of, 85
Communications satellite, 34
Communications Satellite
 Corporation, 37
Condon, Edward U., 85
Corporal (missile), 56,62,63
Coupling, J. J., 35

Douglas, Dr. William, 9,39,48
Drake, Frank D., 70–73,85,87
Dryden, Hugh, 8

Early Bird (communications
 satellite), 37
Echo (satellite), 34,36
Edwards Air Force Base (Muroc
 Air Force Base), 25
Eisenhower, Dwight D., 36
Electron gun, 37
Emperor Franz Joseph, 18
Enos (chimpanzee), 47,52
Epsilon Eridani (star), 71,85
Ercoupe (airplane), 20
EVA (extra vehicular activity),
 58,67,68
Exeter, New Hampshire, 81
Explorer I (satellite), 30,54
Extraterrestrial vehicles, 84

Farman, Henri, 18
Ferguson, Jim, 28
Fisher, Lt. Fink, 15
Flamsteed (crater), 57,64
Floyd Bennett Field, 47
Flying saucer sightings,
 75,84,85,86
Ford, Gerald, 84
Francisco, Ed, 17
Freedom 7, 38,42
Friendship 7, 47

Gagarin, Yuri, 38,41,46,53,57
Gallup, George, 84
Geiger counter, 55
Gemini 3 ("The Molly Brown"),
 45,60
Gemini 4, 58,59,67,68
Gemini 10, 66,68
Gemini program, 9,41,45,50,53,
 58–61, 66–69
G–forces, 22,26,41
Geophysical Year,
 International, 54
Gilruth, Robert, 9,50,66
Glamorous Glennis, 22,23,25
Glenn, John H., Jr., 8,39,46,
 47,52
Goldwater, Barry, 76
Gorgon (missile), 17
Goddard, Esther Kisk
 (Mrs. Robert H.), 10
Goddard, Robert H., 10–13
Goliath (monkey), 46
Green Bank, W. Va., 73
Greenbelt, Md., 13

Grissom, Virgil I., 42–45,
 53,59,60,68
Guadalcanal (carrier), 68
Guggenheim, Daniel, 12
Guggenheim, Harry, 18,19
Guggenheim Aeronautical
 Laboratory, 18,19
Gyroscopes, 12

Haney, Paul, 59
Harvard Observatory, 78
Hillenkoetter, Admiral R. H., 78
Hillsdale College, 82
Hiroshima, 87
Holloman Air Force Base, 26
Holmes, D. Brainerd, 9
House Armed Services
 Committee, 83
Houston Manned Spacecraft
 Center, 50
Hunt Club (helicopters), 43
Hynek, J. Allen, 79,82

Identified Flying Objects
 (IFO's), 79
Intercontinental Ballistic
 Missiles (ICBM's), 46
Institute of Aeronautics and
 Astronautics, 57

Jansky, Karl, 70
JATO (jet-assisted-takeoff),
 17,20,26,28
Jet Propulsion (journal), 35
Jet Propulsion Laboratory,
 36,54,56,62,64,73
Johnson, Lyndon B., 57
Jupiter (planet), 71,80
Jupiter–C (rocket), 30,32,54

Kármán, Theodore von, 18–21,55
Kennedy, John F., 9,21,37,49
Keyhoe, Donald E., 79,82,83
Kimball, Dan, 76
King, John, 82
Kitty Hawk, N.C., 18
Klass, Phillip, 81
Kompfner, Rudolph, 36
Kraft, Christopher C., Jr., 8,50–53
"Kugelblitz", 81

Laika (dog), 30
Lake Champlain (carrier), 38
Langley Field, Hampton, Va., 36
Langley Research Laboratory, 50
Lark (missile), 17
Lasswell, Harold, 87
Lawrence, Lovell, Jr., 14
Leonor, Alexei, 58
Liberty Bell 7, 42
Lindbergh, Charles A., 11
LOX (liquid oxygen), 11,22,24,25
"Lubbock Lights", 78
Luna 9, 57,62,64
Lunar Excursion Module
 (LEM), 58,62

Manned Spacecraft Center,
 41,53,60,66
Mannor, Frank, 81
Marconi, Guglielmo, 73
Mariner 2 (spacecraft), 56,63
Mariner 4, 57
Mars (planet), 57,63
Maser (Microwave Amplification
 by Stimulated Emission of
 Radiation), 71
McDivitt, James, 58,67
McElroy, Neil, 30
McLaughlin, Commander R. B., 86
Medaris, General John, 30
Menninger lectures, 70
Menzel, Donald, 78
Mercury capsule, 38,39,40,46
Mercury Control Center, 48
Mercury program 8,38–49,50
Mescalero Ranch, 12
Millikan, Dr. Robert, 20,55
Misraki, Paul, 85
Mojave Desert, 22
Monkeys, Space, 46,47,52
Moon, 63
Morrison, Dr. Philip, 70
Morse Code, 54
Mueller, Dr. George, 9
Muroc Dry Lake, 22,26
Muscarelo, Norman, 81